After having a breakdown from over-work, career girl Beth was recovering from it all by taking a temporary job looking after Reid McShane and his small son on a farm in Virginia. But it *was* only a temporary situation, until she was fit to go back to her real job. So she had better avoid any emotional entanglements, hadn't she?

GOING
UNDERGROUND

BY
KAREN van der ZEE

MILLS & BOON LIMITED
15–16 BROOK'S MEWS
LONDON W1A 1DR

First published 1982
Australian copyright 1982
Philippine copyright 1983
This edition 1983

© Karen van der Zee 1982

ISBN 0 263 74053 6

Set in Monophoto Plantin 10 on 11½ pt.
01–0183–52676

Made and printed in Great Britain by
Richard Clay (The Chaucer Press) Ltd,
Bungay, Suffolk

CHAPTER ONE

BETH sat at the kitchen table thinking about Reid. He had not asked her why she had come to his farm to take care of his son or what the reason was for the two months' leave of absence from her job. She had been surprised to find a man like him tucked away in a small corner of Southern Virginia. He did not originate from these parts, did not speak the local jargon, did not have the easy drawl of a true Virginian. He was a city man, as she was a city girl.

Sitting here in his beautiful house, Beth waited for him to come home. Like a wife, she thought with faint amusement. His son was in bed, dinner in the oven, coffee on. Another glance at the hardwood kitchen clock told her it was almost nine, and the food in the oven was losing flavour and colour by the minute. If he didn't show up soon it would look like dog food. If she were his wife she'd probably be wondering if he were having an affair with his secretary.

They had met at a Washington dinner party—Doc's party. After twenty minutes of drinks and conversation he had invited her to spend the rest of the summer on his farm taking care of his five-year-old son while he went to work in Richmond. When she'd asked him why he didn't get a teenager to help out, he'd said he preferred someone a little older, especially someone tall with short dark hair and beautiful big blue eyes. He'd smiled at her so winningly that she'd started laughing. And then, to her own surprise, she'd found herself accepting.

Well, she'd rationalised to herself, Doc had insisted she go somewhere for the next couple of months, so why not go to a farm?

She liked Reid. She had instantly fallen in love with his thickly curled hair, his grin, the laughter in his brown eyes. He had the air of someone who didn't care what people said or thought about him. He seemed very comfortable with himself. Tall and lean and straight, he moved with the easy confidence of an athlete.

Next morning, having come to her senses, the heady glow of wind faded from her mind, she telephoned him to call the deal off.

'I've changed my mind,' she informed him in the most businesslike voice she could manage. Not easy. One of her friends had once told her she had a bedroom voice, and knowing that was like a curse. It would haunt her for ever, especially because she did most of her talking outside the bedroom.

'Why?' he asked.

'I had a couple of drinks last night. I've been feeling rotten lately and you marched in and charmed me out of the pits. That's why.'

'Oh.' A slight pause. 'Did you tell me you work in advertising?'

'Yes. What does that have to do with anything?'

Laughter. 'Your message isn't coming across.'

Beth liked the sound of his laughter. She liked his voice, deep and warm. 'You mean you don't under-stand?'

'No. Could you be more specific?'

She groaned inwardly. 'I accepted your invitation on the spur of the moment. It was a hasty decision. I hadn't considered all the consequences and ramifications.' She really hoped she sounded cool and collected and sure of herself. She tried to choose her words carefully. 'I had a good time at the party last night. You were excellent company. However, I don't think that's reason enough to pack a suitcase and move in with you.'

'To take care of my son,' he said dryly.

'Do you think I'm naïve?'

'Obviously not.' The rich tones of his laughter bounced down the line. 'Listen, I made my invitation on the spur of the moment as well, but why don't we give it a try, anyway? You come and take care of my kid, and it will be our mutual understanding that you're not coming to take care of me, so to speak.'

'I'll have to think about it.'

What she had to do was call Doc and ask him who this Reid McShane was, and what he knew about him.

Doc knew plenty. Reid was his nephew, he said. He was a man of character and integrity and all manner of wonderful things. Going to the country, Doc said, would be exactly the right thing for her to do right now. Of course, since she was twenty-six, he didn't need to tell her about the birds and the bees and human nature, and ultimately she'd have to make her own decision.

So Doc was behind it all. It didn't make her mad. He was a family friend, and when needed the family doctor, a man who'd been more like a father to her than her own had ever been. And he wanted her to go to some place quiet and peaceful for a rest.

She had accepted the invitation, naïve or not, and here she was, Beth Anderson, art director in one of Washington's biggest advertising agencies, taking care of a five-year-old boy out in the sticks.

The farm was not really a farm at all. It consisted of several acres of woods, a pasture, a pond surrounded by willow trees and reeds, and a large vegetable garden. There were some chickens, a few bunnies for the boy, a little white milking goat and a golden retriever called Rufus.

And then there was the house. She had never seen a house like this, except in pictures. It was an earth-sheltered building, dug into a softly sloping hill with only the south side exposed. Reid had designed and built it himself and lived in it now, buried in rural Virginia, for heaven knew what reason.

He wasn't a farmer, of course, not with one nanny goat, a few chickens and rabbits. Reid McShane was an architect. A crazy one, she thought, smiling to herself, admiring his style, his go-to-hell attitude.

She heard Reid's car drive up and Rufus's enthusiastic barking, and a moment later Reid burst through the door. He looked tired but happy and Beth's heart gave a curious little leap, as it had at the party when she'd first seen him. There was something about him that triggered in her an instant response every time she saw him.

'Whew! Some day!' he commented obscurely, draping himself on to a kitchen chair.

'Did you have dinner?'

He shook his head, tearing off his tie. 'No, and I'm famished. I'll make myself an omelette or something, but first I'd better take care of poor Phoebe.'

Phoebe was the little white goat. Reid had enclosed part of the pasture for her with an elaborate five-foot-high fence that looked truly invincible. Was it necessary, Beth had asked, to keep the poor innocent little creature locked up like a criminal? Reid had laughed, saying goats were escape artists and he had no intention of giving *poor innocent* Phoebe even the tiniest chance to feast in his garden.

Beth looked doubtfully at the oven. 'I kept some dinner warm for you, but I'm not sure it's edible any more.'

'Of course it is. You're wonderful—absolutely wonderful!' He grinned and strode out of the kitchen, coming back a few minutes later wearing jeans and a work shirt. 'I won't be long.' He opened the kitchen door and went out.

When he came back with the milk Beth took the bucket from him and told him to sit down and eat. 'I'll take care of this.' She poured the milk through a strainer into a large glass jar and put it in the refrigerator while Reid wolfed down his food with appetite.

She poured him a cup of coffee and brought it to the table. Suddenly, without warning, her hand began to tremble violently, and coffee sloshed over the rim and spilled on to the wooden table top. Fear swept through her as her body, too, began to tremble. Her head swam.

'I . . . I'm sorry,' she stammered. 'I . . .' The walls swayed.

In one blurred movement he was up, taking her shoulders, easing her on to a chair.

The dizzy spell passed as quickly as it had begun.

'I'm sorry,' she said again. 'I'm all right now.'

'That's what you said two days ago,' he said dryly.

She didn't want to be reminded. He hadn't asked her what was wrong then; he wasn't asking now. She wondered what Doc had told him. Nothing, of course. Well, how could she be sure?

He was eyeing her closely, slowly drinking his coffee. He probably thought she was pregnant.

'I'm not pregnant,' she said.

Bushy eyebrows rose. 'Did I suggest you were?'

'Isn't that what it seems like?'

'I'll make a positive diagnosis when you start growing a big stomach,' he said, his voice faintly amused.

'I won't!' She felt tight, angry.

He put his cup down. 'Why are you so defensive? You owe me no explanations. A dizzy spell isn't a crime in the Commonwealth of Virginia.'

Why then did she feel she had to make excuses? No, she had not committed a crime, although God knew what the people of Hartford and Grey would call it. Breaking down in the middle of an important presentation, surrounded by hot-shot representatives of a big corporation might not be considered a crime, but it most certainly was unforgivable, intolerable and inexcusable.

A nervous breakdown was what she'd had. Not a proper medical term, but understandable to every layman in the land. Beth Anderson had collapsed, disintegrated in front of a room full of people. Beth Anderson was a nervous wreck—overworked, overburdened, overtired.

I'm a weakling, she thought bitterly, a loser. Can't handle the first big campaign that comes my way. Go all to pieces, crack up like a china cup at the first bit of pressure.

Her work had gained a lot of attention in the last few years. Her ideas were innovative, controversial, a bit daring. Her assignments became bigger and more important. Her work load increased. The pressure increased. The tension increased. She found herself working overtime too often. She worked at home on weekends and holidays.

And then came the freeze-dried coffee account—her first national, multi-media campaign, and everything grew worse. The work coming from the art department, her superiors said, was a bit *too* controversial, a bit *too* daring. There were daily battles with the copy department; with artists and photographers; with Jack, the account executive who was terrified he'd lose his new account, and who shouted at her that it wasn't up to her to tell the copy department what to do and what to write. Which was true.

God, she'd thought furiously, what the hell can you do with instant coffee? She'd found something and it was making her a wreck.

In the end she'd gained some and she'd lost some. In the weeks before the presentation she'd been able to sleep only a few hours a night, her mind too busy worrying and agonising. Her stomach cramped every time she thought about the presentation. Doughnuts and coffee seemed all she was able to eat. Her days were filled with arguments, disagreements, tension. And all for instant coffee, she'd thought in a saner moment. The world had gone berserk around her. She herself had gone berserk.

'How about a drink?'

'I'd rather have coffee.' She stood up. 'I'll do it.'

'You sit.'

She sat. He took the dishes to the counter and poured coffee. His back was turned to her. Nice back—wide, strong. Her eyes settled on the brown mop of hair with its thick, tight curls. It sat on his head like an invitation: *Touch me.* She'd love to.

He turned and handed her a cup.

He was a capable man, Reid, raising Josh alone, and keeping house himself with only the help of a local woman who came in now and then to give the place a good cleaning. He had no talent for that, Reid had said, grinning. Beth had the suspicion that if he set his mind to it he could do as well as anybody.

And then there was Grandma Daisy who lived in

the next house down the road. Big, tall and strong, she had no resemblance to a daisy. She and Reid had struck a bartering arrangement. Grandma Daisy would bake his bread and can his vegetables and babysit Josh now and then, and Reid would give her milk and eggs, cut her a supply of firewood, and sweep her chimney.

She wondered how long Reid had been alone and what had happened to his wife. Were they divorced? Had she left him? Was she dead? What did *she* care? She was here to patch up her frazzled emotions in peace and quiet. What better place than this? Rolling green countryside, a beautiful, comfortable house, a vegetable garden, chickens, a goat, a dog. And a boy who didn't want her around.

'Josh doesn't like me. You know that?'

He grinned. 'Give him time. He's not used to having females around the house. I'm afraid he might have some lopsided ideas about the place of women in life. Another reason your presence here might not be amiss.' He stacked the dishes in the dishwasher and closed it. 'Sorry I was so late tonight. Thanks for keeping some dinner for me.'

'Another advantage of having a female around the house.'

His eyes laughed into hers. 'I wouldn't dream of saying such a thing.'

'Ah, a liberated male!'

He laughed wryly. 'You could say that.' He paused. 'Would you like to go for a walk?'

Every night, after Josh was asleep and darkness set in, he would go out. He had not invited her to come with him before.

'Is it all right to leave Josh alone in the house?' she asked.

'I always stay within earshot. I just wander around

the house, check on the chickens and rabbits. He knows.'

It was a warm summer night, the air warmer outside than in. It was amazing how cool the house was without air-conditioning. A week ago the weather had been blistering hot with a temperature of over a hundred degrees in the shade, and the house had been comfortably cool. It was almost impossible for outdoor air to penetrate the mass of soil around and on top of the house.

Beth was fascinated by the house, having thought an earth-sheltered house would be damp and dark, and found it the exact opposite. The front of the house, the south side, was made almost entirely of glass windows that could be shaded in summer without much loss of light. There were skylights in the bedrooms in the back of the house and in the daytime the place was as light and cheerful as any above-ground house.

She liked the interior, which was furnished comfortably and casually. It was a place to feel at home in, a place where people lived, with lots of books and magazines and toys lying around.

They walked along the path to the hen house and the rabbit hutches, found everything in order, then crossed the pasture to the pond and sat down on the dock. Beth saw the dark shape of the little rubber boat and remembered Josh sitting in it that afternoon, moving it up and down, looking at her on the dock, his eyes bright with defiance. Five years old and he knew exactly what he did and did not want. One thing he did not want was to have her around. His whole attitude towards her was hostile and rebellious. She'd been afraid he'd fall in the water and he had known it.

The dock was very small and Reid was very close. She was aware of him physically every time he was near her. His presence set off tiny sparks all through her. She was conscious of her own body in the most intense way, as if she were suddenly overly sensitive, as if every nerve stood at attention. She tried hard to ignore it.

'Aren't you afraid having the pond so close to the house?' she asked, looking straight out over the water. 'What if Josh takes off by himself and starts playing by the water, fooling around in that boat?'

'He's safe enough, swims like a shrimp, the shrimp. Taught him myself when he was still a baby.'

She pictured him in the water playing with his baby son, laughing, making funny sounds and faces, splashing water.

'Do you like living out here in the country?' He seemed to. She was intrigued by his life style. He was a strange man. Not weird-strange, but rather interesting-strange. A small thrill went through her—excitement, apprehension. He was next to her in the dark, very close, and all she had to do was move her leg or arm and they'd be touching. The thought alone was so overwhelming, so enticing that a sudden fear rushed through her. She tightened her muscles, sat stiffly staring out into the dark, fearful her body might betray her and act out its wishes without the benefit of her reason.

This is ridiculous, she told herself. You're crazy. So what if you touch him? Is that a crime? You're twenty-six. He won't be the first man you've ever touched.

She took a deep breath and tried to relax, hearing Reid's words calmly flowing out into the night in answer to her question. Yes, he liked living in the country, thought it was a good place for his son to grow up.

'All my life, as a child and as an adult, I lived in an

apartment, until five years ago,' he said. 'I bought this property soon after Josh was born, built myself this house. It was something I'd always wanted to do, build an earth-sheltered home—underground, instead of twelve stories above. One thing led to another. I became interested in alternative energy, especially solar and wind power.' Part of his electricity was generated by a windmill he had built two years ago. It was a tall, metal structure, looking rather out of place.

Beth looked at him sideways. 'And then the natural progression to a garden, chickens, a goat, etcetera,' she offered.

He laughed. 'As long as I was living out in the boondocks I decided I might as well go all the way, see how self-sufficient I could become. Actually, I had a very deprived childhood, you see, living high up, thinking milk came from the supermarket and eggs were manufactured in a factory.' His voice held humour.

'I grew up in a high-rise, too. How come I don't feel sorry for you?'

'Maybe you should try harder.' He threw a pebble into the pond. It was a soft sloshy plop and in the moonlight she could vaguely see the rings in the water widening. It was so very peaceful here. No roar of traffic, no sirens. No constant ringing of telephones or the shouting of overexcited, angry, nervous or neurotic people around her. Her office had been a madhouse the week before the presentation. She'd fit right in with all the other neurotics, of course.

It all seemed so unreal now, so far removed from her life here. She let out a deep sigh and let her glance travel over the darkened landscape. A half moon. Silhouettes of the tall evergreens protecting the north side of the house, like sentinels. Crickets chirping in the grass. The faint rustling of the weeping willow hanging over the dock and pond.

Doc had been right—this was the perfect place for her to calm down and get herself back together again. But why had Reid invited her? True enough, he needed someone to watch Josh while he was working, but any teenager could have done that.

'Why did you ask me to come here, Reid?' The question had lingered in her mind ever since the arrangement had been made. He had made no passes at her, taken no advantage of the situation. Was she being naïve?

'Because I needed somebody to keep an eye on Josh while I got myself into business again.' He looked at her sideways. 'That's what we agreed upon, wasn't it?'

'You didn't even know me.'

He laughed. 'When I met you at Doc's party I liked you right from the start, to say it decently. And any friend of Doc's is good enough for me.' He paused. 'Of course, it was all on impulse,' he said then. 'It came to me suddenly, some wild idea that it might be good for Josh to have a regular female influence in the house for a while. It's always been just the two of us, ever since he was born.'

Had his wife died in childbirth? Beth pushed the thought aside.

'Doc set this up, didn't he?' she asked.

He laughed. 'If he did he was certainly very discreet about it.'

'What did he tell you about me?'

'What do you think he told me? Nothing, of course. All he said was that you wanted to get out of town for a while. I took one look at you and decided I knew just the place for you to go.' He grinned. 'Not that I expected you to accept, of course.'

'You sweet-talked me over a few glasses of wine. With me anything is possible then ... forget I said that.'

He roared. 'No, I have to remember that.'

'You'd better not. And besides, you have to give me credit for cancelling out the next day, when I'd come to my senses.'

'You *tried* to call if off, but you're *here*. Thanks to my powers of persuasion.'

'You're unbearably arrogant,' she told him.

'Thank you,' he said soberly. 'Anything else?'

'No. Yes. Why didn't you expect me to accept?'

'Have you ever heard of a big-time career girl going to some Virginia backwater to babysit a five-year-old spoiled brat?'

Beth grinned to herself. 'You put it very graphically! No, I don't suppose I·have.'

'You must be the very first in the modern history of the new liberated, emancipated female.'

Something had gone wrong. His words didn't quite hit right. 'I'm not sure how liberated I am sometimes.' The bitterness in her voice came as a shock even to herself.

The words lingered in the silence.

'What do you mean by that?' Reid asked after a pause.

'I'm not so sure I've gone my own liberated way. I did what was expected of me. I was *supposed* to make something of myself, get in the rat race and scramble to get ahead. I was *supposed* to have a career—something meaningful in terms of money and esteem. Talk about choices; I don't think I really ever had one.'

Now why had she said that? Why was she suddenly erupting in these negative thoughts, spilling them like dirty laundry? For a long time she had kept them to herself, not knowing what to do with all the anger and hostility she had felt building up all through her growing years—anger and hostility towards her father. the crushing feeling, too, of being a failure in his eyes, of not measuring up to his expectations.

Her grades in school had never been good enough. Her mind's eye still held the picture of her father's face as he looked at her report cards, his eyes settled on the barely average grades for math and science. He was always pressuring her to do better, saying Cs weren't good enough, never saying much. about her high marks in Art, Social Sciences, English.

'But, Daddy, I got an A in Art! An A in English!' Her voice still rang in her memory, the sound of painful disappointment still there.

That was nice, he'd say without any real appreciation, but Maths and Science were what counted, because without them she'd never get anywhere.

Well, she'd got somewhere, but he hadn't lived to see it. A high-powered businessman with both hands in the political arena, he had died of a massive heart attack five years ago.

He hadn't been happy with her choice of college, her choice of courses, but he had paid nonetheless. Beth had felt some kind of bitter triumph that at least she had won that battle, but the feeling of his pressure for performance had never left her. Whatever she would do in life, whatever career she chose, she would have to be the best. His eyes would follow her always. Even if in reality he had no hold on her, she would always feel his presence, his pressure. Even now that he was dead.

She took a deep breath. The air was fragrant with summer scents. The water shimmered darkly in the moonlight, and a soft wind brushed her cheeks. A beautiful night, and next to her on the dock was Reid. Tomorrow she'd still be here, and the day after. It was a calming thought.

'Do you like your work?' Reid's voice was even. He had been quiet for some time.

'I do, and I don't. Sometimes I hate it. Sometimes I wish I didn't have to face the day and go back to the office.'

'How old are you?'

'Twenty-six.'

'And already on your way to high blood pressure, ulcers . . . for what?'

'Instant coffee,' she said promptly.

He roared, head thrown back. And then she was laughing too, feeling herself relax into tranquil relief. No more reflection, no more sombre, depressing thoughts.

Reid had stopped laughing and he was looking at her, eyes still smiling. He leaned over to her, his face very close.

'May I give you a bit of advice?' he whispered.

'What?' Why was her heart pounding?

'Don't waste your health and sanity on instant coffee. Believe me, it isn't worth it.' And then he kissed her.

It was no surprise. The vibrations had been there ever since they'd stepped out into the warm night. But unprepared for the impact of his touch, a flood of sweet, thrilling excitement surged through her. Except for his mouth he was not touching her at all, giving his kiss a sensuous and mysterious quality. She felt as if she were floating through the silence of the night. All she was aware of were his lips caressing hers, the warmth of his mouth, her heart beating wildly in her chest . . . only him, only her. The moment was pure magic.

She opened her eyes when she no longer felt the warmth of his mouth. His face was only inches away and the magic was still there. She sat perfectly still as in a hypnotic trance. Reid looked at her silently and it was like a dream, a fantasy, for what she saw in his eyes was beautiful and perfect. The idyllic night, the serenity of their surroundings enveloped them with a velvety softness that faded out any reality.

'Beth . . .' He reached out and touched the top of her head, smoothing his hand down the short length of hair until it came to rest on the bare back of her neck. The warmth of his hand spread all the way through her. She didn't dare look at him, afraid of she knew not what. A sweet shiver ran down her spine.

Slowly he removed his hand. Beth stole a quick glance at him, her heart in her throat. His face was set in serious contemplation.

She wanted him close so badly it hurt, and she was suddenly terrified by her own overpowering emotions. She wasn't a newcomer in the land of love and romance, but the strength of her emotions and reactions to even the simplest of kisses was totally alien to her. God, she thought, I'm going crazy. There's something wrong with me. She took a deep steadying breath.

Reid turned his head, surveying her for a moment.

'You're not here because of a man, are you?'

The question surprised her. 'No. Why?'

'Just asking. Ever been married?'

'No.'

'Too busy?'

'I don't know.' She thought for a moment. 'No, not too busy. I had a couple of opportunities, but I had to turn them down. Awful!'

Paul's face swam into her memory, the despair in his eyes. Saying no to him had been one of the most difficult things she'd ever had to do.

'Why awful?'

'Last year a man wanted to marry me. He loved me—I know he really did. I had to say no and it was terribly painful.'

'You didn't love him?'

'For a while I thought I did. He was a wonderful man, nice, and fun to be with, but . . .' She sighed and smiled at the same time. 'He wasn't right for me.'

'Not handsome enough? Not rich enough?' His voice was mildly teasing.

She grinned. 'I should push you in the water for that!'

'Try it.'

'I have no illusions.' He was well over six feet tall and weighed close to two hundred pounds if her guess was any good. She was tall, but with her hundred and twenty pounds she was no match for him.

'Haven't you heard of the ant who moved the rubber tree plant?' he asked.

'And the ram who punched a hole in the dam?'

'Right.'

'My hopes aren't that high.' There was no way she was going to wrestle with him on this dock.

He sighed. 'Okay, I give. So what happened to that first lover of yours? I know I'm not supposed to ask, but I will anyway.'

'He didn't really count. He only wanted my body.'

He gave a hearty laugh. 'Don't we all?'

'I do still have illusions about that. I keep hoping some men got liberated along with the women.'

'Not a man-hater, are you? I didn't think so.'

'There are two and a half billion men in this world,

give or take a few billion. I'm sure there are a few
good ones hidden somewhere.'

'I know one hidden in a house underground. A very
good one.'

'What are you after? My body?'

He grinned. 'You wouldn't want that, would you?'

'Didn't we just have that discussion?'

Laughing, Reid jumped to his feet. He reached out
his hand and pulled her up. 'We'd better get back.'

He whistled for the dog, who came loping from
somewhere out of the darkness.

They walked to the house, not talking, not touching.

Beth watched Reid milk the goat. It was early in the
morning. She was surprised to find that she enjoyed
getting up early these days. Normally, getting out of
bed was a struggle that repeated itself every morning.
Never a good beginning. She had always envied people
who started the day with a song and a smile. For her,
two cups of coffee and something sweet and sugary,
like doughnuts or coffee cake, were necessary to even
start her thinking or talking.

Having heard of her atrocious diet in the morning
Reid wouldn't let her come close to the stove. He fed
her eggs and ham, or wholewheat cereal with milk and
fruit. She had refused the first few mornings, but soon
developed an appetite just watching Reid and Josh
devouring their food.

It was a wonderful sunny morning, colouring the
landscape with a veil of bright gold. Arms around her
knees, Beth sat in the grass, watching the little white
goat, seeing Reid's large hands extracting the milk. It
squirted out in thin streams into the shiny, stainless
steel bucket.

She became aware of an unpleasant feeling. The seat

of her jeans was wet. Damn! She jumped up. 'This stupid grass is wet!'

'Of course it's wet,' Reid smiled patiently. 'It's called dew.'

'How am I supposed to know? I grew up in the middle of glass, steel and concrete. Grass was no part of my environment.'

'That bad, huh?'

She sighed theatrically. 'Oh, well, let's just say I wasn't thinking when I sat down. By the time I usually get up dew has long gone.' She rubbed her posterior. 'Yuk, this feels terrible!'

'Go and change and I'll teach you how to gather eggs. They're manufactured by chickens, in case you didn't learn that either.'

In the next few days Beth learned a lot of things. How to milk Phoebe the goat, where the chickens hid their eggs, how to fish for bass in the pond.

There was more to fishing than she'd imagined. Sitting quietly on the banks of a stream or staring out over the waters of a calm lake, dreaming up solutions for the world's problems wasn't all. First of all one had to learn how to cast the bait (and worse, how to put the bait on the hook).

'Like *this*,' Reid explained. 'Throw it in one smooth flowing movement, depress and release, and there it goes.' He demonstrated flawlessly. It seemed easy enough. Even Josh, who sat away from them, ignoring them blatantly, could do it. Beth tried. It wasn't quite so easy. Bait and line ended up everywhere except far out in the water. It got caught in the weeping willow, in the reeds by the water. It dropped kerplonk right in front of her in the pond. She was getting exasperated, not to mention embarrassed. Reid looked on, his face expressionless, but his eyes were gleaming with humour. She glared at him.

'You're not laughing at me by any chance, are you?'

He gave her an innocent look. 'Me? I never laugh at honest effort.'

'I'll bet,' she retorted bitterly, reeling in the line after another fruitless attempt. The hook and bait came up, dragging along a glob of muck.

Eventually she did figure it out and was able to cast the bait in a half-way acceptable fashion. Of course it wasn't she who did the catching, but Reid. He consoled her by saying the fish didn't know her yet and were slightly distrustful. She'd do better next time.

Beth squirmed uneasily as she watched Reid clean the fish. 'I think I can live without learning how to do that. It's barbaric!'

'Don't visit the slaughterhouses in Chicago,' he advised.

'I've heard about them, and that's enough all by itself.'

The fish was ready to cook. 'I'll fry them,' she offered, 'I am good at that.'

'All right, I'll get the fixings for the salad.' He left for the garden.

It was wonderful to work in this kitchen, Beth thought. Lots of counter space, plenty of cupboards, and all the modern appliances including a large freezer.

She sprinkled salt and pepper on the fish, dipped it in egg, then in flour. Soft footsteps came from behind her, then Josh's little face appeared by her side.

'I don't like it that way,' he said, his voice as well as his face hostile.

'Have you ever had it this way?'

'No.'

'How do you know you don't like it, then?'

'I can see it. It looks awful!'

'I'm sorry.' She smiled at him, showing no offence. 'Maybe you'll like the dessert. I made it specially for you.'

'I won't like it.'

'You don't even know what it is.'

His chin lifted stubbornly. 'I won't like it anyway. It's probably *disgusting*!'

It was hard to keep her face straight and not laugh. Instinct told her that it was crucial to take him seriously. If she wounded his pride and self-esteem all would be lost. She still had hopes of winning him over.

'I wish you'd never come here,' he said, apparently intent on making her lose her composure. 'I wish I could just stay with Grandma Daisy while my dad is gone. I always did before, you know.'

Because your dad wasn't gone as often, she answered silently. Now he's gone almost every day.

There was no sense in arguing with him, so she did not reply. Carefully she arranged the fish in the melted butter in the pan.

Reid came back from the garden with a harvest of cherry tomatoes, lettuce, green onions and parsley. He put it all in the sink and rinsed everything quickly. No need to worry about fertilisers and insecticides, he had told her. Mother nature took care of this lot. It was a pretty garden, protected against unwanted visitors by marigolds, garlic, onions and a variety of herbs.

The meal was delicious. Beth was a good cook when she put her mind to it. She enjoyed preparing meals for others, although she hardly ever made much effort for herself alone. Josh ate without comment. He was hungry, she could tell. The dessert, a light concoction made of fresh peaches, went down without complaint.

They had coffee while watching the evening news on TV. Josh played quietly with his Lego blocks, sitting on the floor at his father's feet. He looked small and vulnerable. Poor little kid. '*It's always been just the two of us, ever since he was born.*' Reid's words flowed back into her consciousness.

Beth turned her attention back to the news, seeing the sharp face of Stuart Engleton appear on the screen. 'Him again,' she muttered. Stuart Engleton, famous prosecuting attorney—admired, feared, hated.

'He has a new case,' Reid commented. 'Controversial as usual.'

'He looks like a vulture.'

He laughed. 'He *is* a vulture. But you have to admire the man for his genius. He doesn't often lose a case.'

'I object to his methods. He could make a newborn baby look like a perverted criminal.' She grimaced. 'They ought to lock him up in the bird house!'

He grinned at her, his eyes amused.

A toothpaste commercial interrupted the newscast and Beth stood up. 'Want more coffee?'

'No, thanks.'

'I made a full pot—you're sure?'

'Positive. There's no obligation for you to down the entire pot though.'

'I like coffee.'

'So I've noticed.'

Beth marched out. The faint censure in his voice had not escaped her. So she drank too much coffee. Was it any of his business? At work it was the only thing that kept her going. She had her own coffee pot in her office and it was always on. People were coming and going all day long and having a cup in her hand was better than a cigarette and more attractive than twirling hair or biting nails.

She filled her cup. God, just thinking of work gave her the shakes. Coffee of course didn't help. Cut down on the stuff, Doc had instructed. Make you sleep better too. She looked at the pot more than half full of rich dark brew. She unplugged it, took the decanter and poured the coffee down the sink, eyes closed tightly.

She wondered what had happened to the freeze-dried coffee account. It had been in her mind ever since she'd left Washington, but she'd been too much of a coward to call Jack and find out. No one knew where she was, so he wouldn't have been able to contact her even if he had wanted. She would call him and end the suspense. She'd already poured half a pot of coffee down the sink, so this was her night for bravery, it seemed.

The news over, Reid instructed Josh to pick up his toys and get ready for bed.

Beth got up. 'Do you mind if I make a long-distance phone call? D.C.,' she specified.

He waved at the door of his study. 'Do it in there if you like.' He followed Josh to help him with his bedroom routine.

Beth went into the study, sat down at the desk and stared at the telephone. She'd have to call Jack at home, although it was possible he was still at his office, she supposed. Or just about anywhere. Divorced from his wife years ago, he led a haphazard sort of life, spending most of his time at the office. He skipped meals, drank too much, smoked continuously and functioned on nothing but adrenalin.

Beth picked up the receiver and punched the buttons with more force than bravery. Her heart was racing.

He answered the phone almost immediately and blew up the minute he realised who she was.

'Where the hell *are* you!' he shouted.

'In Hong Kong,' she shot back. 'Jack . . .'

'Dammit, I've looked all over creation for you! Where are you?' He sounded as if he wanted to jump right through the phone.

'Can you stop shouting? I can *hear* you!'

'Beth . . .' his voice sounded threatening.

'Jack, I went away on doctor's orders, remember? Don't give me any grief or I'll hang up.'

'Don't hang up!' he said hastily.

'All right. Now why did you want to know where I am? You want to fire me?'

'Fire you?' His voice seemed faintly surprised. 'Hell, no. I want to know how you're doing, and when you're coming back to work.'

'I'm fine as long as I don't think about work. I'm not coming back for a while yet, you know that.'

'It's been a couple of weeks, for God's sake! Haven't you got yourself straightened out yet?'

Beth clenched her jaws. 'No. And I don't want to talk about it any more. I'm calling you to find out about the coffee account.'

'We got it, of course.'

Relief almost made her dizzy. '*Of course?*'

'It was brilliant,' he told her. 'You had a great new angle.'

'I also had a nervous breakdown right in front of everybody.'

'Who cares? You know what the old buzzard said?'

'I have an idea I'm not going to like this,' said Beth wryly.

He laughed. 'He said this sort of thing is to be expected from women in business. They're creative and artistic. Also neurotic, highly strung, and prone to crying.'

'The bastard! He probably wouldn't have cared if

I'd dropped dead in front of him as long as the campaign looked good.'

Jack laughed. 'Probably.'

'It's a lovely business we're in,' she said dryly.

'Life is hell.'

She heard a sound of ice in a glass. 'Are you drinking again?'

'Sure, what else? You want to come over and join me? We could celebrate.'

'No, thanks.'

'Too far away, right? Where are you? What are you doing?'

'I've gone fishing.'

A pause. 'They tell me it's very relaxing. What are you fishing for?'

'Bass.'

'Where?'

'Hong Kong, I told you.'

'You're not going to tell me, are you?'

'No. All I wanted to know was what happened to the account. And I know now, so I'll say goodnight. Goodnight, Jack.' Beth hung up.

She looked at her hands, seeing them tremble. What had happened to her in the last few years? She'd never been neurotic or highly strung. Look at her hands now. She was a wreck. She closed her eyes. They'd won the coffee account. *They'd won the coffee account!* The fear of the last weeks drained out of her. Head on her arms, she burst into tears.

CHAPTER TWO

SHE cried herself into exhaustion. Head still on her arms, she tried to steady her breathing and calm her shuddering body. Not since she had broken down at the presentation had she cried like this. And before that? She couldn't even remember. She wasn't a crier. When things got bad she would take a deep breath, grit her teeth and get through them.

What had happened in those past few years? Common sense and determination didn't work any more. She felt weak and out of control. When was she going to feel normal again? Normal, what was that? That constant state of anxiety she'd felt for the last few years? The nervous tension? The sleepless nights?

She raised her head and wiped her eyes and blew her nose. There was a sudden awareness of something in the room, another presence. Looking around slowly, she saw Reid, his tall body comfortably stretched out in an easy chair. Hands folded behind his head, he studied her calmly.

Anger and embarrassment nearly choked her. How long had he been here in this room? How long had he been sitting there, watching her? How dared he!

'I heard you,' he said calmly, as if he had anticipated her outrage. 'It seemed rather cold-blooded to walk past the door and pretend I didn't hear you. I thought you might want a shoulder.' He patted his own. 'This one is broad and very comfortable.'

Beth shoved back the desk chair and came to her feet, legs trembling. 'I hope you're having fun,' she said bitterly. Turning on her heel, she started for the door, but he was with her in a flash, taking her shoulders and turning her to face him.

'I didn't mean to hurt or offend you.' His eyes were without laughter. 'There's nothing remotely amusing about hearing you cry like you did. And I *did* come in here because I thought I might do some good. Grief and pain are sometimes very lonely emotions, aren't they?' His eyes held hers and she couldn't look away. Slowly his arms slid around her back and he pulled her to him. Anger and resentment melted away as by magic. Automatically she moved her arms around him and his back felt warm and strong under her hands. It was good standing there with her face against his shoulder, good to feel his comfort. She'd felt so fragile lately, so out of control. It terrified her. Now, for this moment at least, she felt safe and cared for.

It seemed hours later when Reid stirred and moved his face against hers. 'How's my shoulder?' he whispered.

She couldn't help smiling. 'Nice and broad and very comfortable.'

'I thought so.' He moved away a little and smiled into her eyes.

Beth lowered her face. She must look dreadful, red and swollen from all that crying. 'I'm sorry.'

'You keep saying that. Let's go to the living room and have a drink and we can talk, if you want to. Or we can just watch a movie on TV. There's a good one on tonight.'

She caught the glint in his eyes. 'Which one?'

'*Tarzan and the Monster from Outer Space.*'

Glass in hand, Beth looked around the room, not seeing anything, just splashes of colour—the green of a large fern hanging from the ceiling, the bright blue of a book jacket, the mixed colours of Josh's toys in the corner. She sipped from the Scotch and fixed her eyes on the fern.

'I cracked up in the middle of a presentation,' she told Reid. 'The one for the coffee account. It happened a few days before I met you at Doc's party.' She closed her eyes. 'I couldn't believe it. It was the worst thing that ever happened to me.'

Reid made no comment. He stood by the large window, one hand on his hip, the other holding his glass.

'I was standing up, talking, explaining something, and then suddenly my mind went blank. I began to shake, really shake, and I couldn't do a thing about it. It was terrifying, all those eyes looking at me. And then . . . then . . . I started crying. I lost all control. All I could do was stand there, shaking and crying until somebody took me away.' She took another sip from her glass, her eyes down. 'It was humiliating! I felt such a fool, breaking down like a kid.'

'Why did it happen?'

She shrugged. 'Stress, Doc said. I'd been under too much pressure.' She laughed bitterly. 'The whole world, all of life, is full of stress and pressure. Why can't I take it? Why do I have to crack?'

'Why not?'

His question took her by surprise. 'What do you mean why not? I feel like a loser, a damn failure! I should be able to cope with modern business life! That's the way I was brought up! Go out there and succeed!'

'And make lots of money and die of a coronary when you're forty-five?' he added soberly. 'In case you didn't know, the rate of heart attacks in women is going up very quickly these days. Guess why.'

She stared at him for a long moment. 'What do you mean?'

'Do we all have to climb the proverbial ladder? Do we all have to be bulldozers?'

'What are you trying to tell me? Should I give up and start weaving baskets?'

'What's wrong with weaving baskets?'

'Nothing! But it isn't the point!'

'Tell me, do you like your job? Are you enjoying it?'

'Do I enjoy it? Oh, lord, you should have seen me those last few years!' Her hands cramped around her glass. 'No, I don't enjoy it, not any more. Oh, at first, yes, at first it was fun. I started off as a lowly copy writer at a very small agency. Did layout work too. Now that was fun. I learned fast, and I was good, really good. So what happened? Before I knew it I was an art director in a big agency. Oh, the big time! My own office, several people working under me, responsibility, and money—oh yes, a nice respectable salary. Got myself a better apartment, a better car, some new furniture.' She looked up at the ceiling blinking furiously.

'You sound positively delighted,' he drawled.

She didn't reply.

'It doesn't seem like such a happy story.'

She glanced back at him, smiling ruefully. 'It should be, shouldn't it?'

'If that's what you really wanted, then yes, it should have been.'

'Of course I wanted it! Doesn't everybody? Why work your tail off and not get anywhere?'

'The only problem is that you don't always get where you thought you wanted to be.'

'I wanted to be where I am! And I worked *hard* to get there!'

Reid shifted his weight from one foot to the other. 'Don't be so damned defensive, Beth,' he said impatiently. 'I'm not questioning the fact that you worked hard. Sometimes plans don't work out. Sometimes things aren't what we thought they'd be. Sometimes, Beth, we have to rearrange our lives because circumstances require it.' He had spoken slowly, looking straight at her. She had the strangest feeling he was speaking about himself.

For a moment she regarded him silently, then looked away, focusing her eyes on the fern once more. 'I don't know what to do,' she said tonelessly. 'I think . . . I hope I'll be all right after a while. I want to go back and try again.' She looked back at him. 'You see, I can't just give up. I don't want to be a loser. I want to prove I can do it.'

'You don't have to prove anything to anybody,' he said evenly. He drained his glass. 'I didn't mean to upset you even more. I just thought it might help to talk.' He strode across the room towards his study. 'I'm going to make a few phone calls.'

Discussion closed.

Beth made a face at his retreating back. Shrink! she said silently. You should go into psychotherapy. Blooming business, so I hear.

He could set up office in the Freud Hilton on Connecticut Avenue in Washington. One more psychiatrist in Shrink City wouldn't make a difference. She could see him in her mind's eye in a fancy office with designer furniture, Oriental carpets and a flashy blonde receptionist. She'd never been inside one (although maybe it was time to go), but she'd heard the stories.

She was being childish, and she knew it, but it made

her feel better just the same. Childish, yes, and quite unfair too.

She envied Reid his self-confidence, his self-assurance. He was in control of himself and his life—no one told him anything. He was a free man, not tied to the demands and expectations of others. He did as he pleased.

Beth got up and turned on the TV, switching it from channel to channel, finding nothing of interest. Ah, there was the movie—*Tarzan and the Monster from Outer Space*. Oh, well, why not? Curling up on the sofa, she let out a martyred sigh and fixed her eyes on the screen.

Almost every morning Reid left the house after he had taken care of the animals. He spent most of his day in Richmond where he was setting up a corporation with some of his friends. For years he had been working on the development of a piece of property near Richmond, which would include the construction of thirty earth-sheltered family homes.

Josh wasn't used to having his father out of reach so much of the time. He wasn't happy to be left with Beth. He was strong-willed and not easy to handle, but she managed, mostly using calm determination and persistence.

'I don't like you!' he cried when Beth was strict with him about watching too much TV. 'I don't like you!'

'I'm very sorry about that.'

'I'm going to tell my dad I want you to go away!' His dark eyes spit fire at her. Small fists were clenched by his side. Beth felt sorry for his underlying sense of fear. He saw her as a threat—a threat to the small safe world his father and he had created together. No one was allowed to invade it.

'I think you should tell him,' she said quietly. 'I think it's important that he knows how you feel, Josh.' Her voice was very gentle and he looked at her suspiciously.

'If my dad sends you away, are you gonna go?'

'Of course. This isn't my home, Josh. I'm only a guest for a little while.'

Was there relief in his eyes? More than anything she wanted to put her arms around him and hold him, tell him she wouldn't hurt him, would never hurt him. She watched his angry little body slowly relax. His proud little chin lifted in a gesture of defiance and he shrugged one shoulder indifferently.

'Oh, well, I guess it's all right then.'

She knew what he meant. It was all right because she was only a guest. Because she wasn't going to stay.

'I don't like you!' Josh repeated a few days later.

'I'm really sorry.' Was he trying to make her angry?

His shrug held contempt. 'You don't even know anything about rabbits!'

The rabbits were his and he took care of them almost singlehandedly. Beth had watched him clean the cages, feed them, fill the water bottles. He had been aware of her watching him and she'd noticed the pride in his face, his whole body.

'Nobody ever taught me anything about rabbits,' she said. 'I didn't even have a dog or a cat when I was little.'

His eyes widened. 'No? No pets at all?'

She shook her head. 'I lived in an apartment. There was no yard or pasture or anything. We had a balcony, that's all. No room for pets.'

'You could have had a cat!'

'My mother didn't like cats.'

'Oh.' He seemed impressed. He stared at her silently

for a while, all manner of thoughts and emotions racing through his mind, she could tell by the shifting expressions in his eyes and face.

'I never had a mother,' he said then. 'My father said she had to go away after I was born, so he took care of me. He says taking care of me is the most important job in the whole wide world. So I know he'll never go away and leave me.' His voice was very calm, very sure.

Beth felt a rush of emotion go through her. 'He loves you very much.'

'I know,' Josh said calmly. He looked very sure of himself. 'He tells me all the time.'

There was no doubt in her mind that it was so. Never had she seen a father and son so close. It was good to see the two together, playing, working, talking. It was obvious that Josh was the most important part of Reid's life.

'Josh,' she said after a silence, 'would you like to help me bake some chocolate chip cookies?'

His face lit up. 'Can I stir in the chips?'

She feigned a worried look. 'Are you good at that?'

He straightened his body. 'Ha! I'm the best stirrer in the whole world!'

Reid was pleased that night. Work had gone well and most of the legal red tape was taken care of now. He seemed eager to talk about the happenings of the day, and later that night, he showed Beth maps and blueprints with all the details of the project.

'Are you sure the world is ready for this?' she asked. 'People have very wrong impressions about underground houses. I was one of them.'

'You *were*. You're not any more. People can come

and see for themselves when the first units are finished. Low utility bills will be a draw all by themselves. Part of the electricity will be generated by windmills. Heating and cooling needs will be minimal to begin with because of the construction methods.'

She knew that already, but she let him talk.

'We'll go small at first, like I said. Here, look at this.' Reid pointed at a map pinned to the wall. 'We'll build three streets with ten units apiece. They all have to face south, or slightly south-east, of course, so the streets have to be more or less straight. We have three different designs, though, so there'll be some variety. All the houses will look out on the back hill of the house in front—nice and green. Gives a sense of privacy too, and that's important, of course.' He showed her another map. 'Here's the landscaping. On the north side of each house we'll plant some evergreen trees as an extra buffer against the north wind. The streets will be wide enough so the trees won't block the sun from the houses behind.'

He gazed at the map for a moment, thinking. Then he looked up at her and grinned. 'Actually, the world doesn't have to be ready for this. Only thirty buyers will do.'

'How are you going to get those thirty?' she asked.

'There'll be plenty of publicity, I'm not worried about that.' He shrugged. 'There's always a risk, of course. I'm not sure, for instance, that Richmond is the best location for this kind of venture, but that's where it'll have to be, for various reasons.'

'It's terribly exciting, isn't it?'

'This stuff doesn't bore you to tears?'

'Oh, no. Not after spending weeks with instant coffee on my mind.' Beth looked at the papers on his desk, seeing in her mind the small development all finished and ready. She tapped the paper. 'I'll bet this is going to be beautiful.'

'You think so?' He was balancing himself on a corner of his desk, leaning on one hand. Her eyes were on that strong brown hand, close to her own, and she wanted to take it and hold it.

She raised her face. 'Oh, I do. See what you did with your own house. And if you're incorporated then I can buy shares, can't I?'

He nodded slowly, his eyes laughing into hers. 'Are you ready to risk your money in a scheme like this?'

'They tell me that's what life is all about, taking risks.'

He leaned over and his face was so close, she thought her heart would stop. There was something half serious, half laughing in his eyes, and a thrill of anticipation went through her.

There was an unbearable silence.

'You're an exciting lady,' he whispered. 'Would you like to go for a walk in the moonlight?'

'That's pretty risky, isn't it?' she whispered back.

Reid laughed softly and took her hand and led her out of the house and around the back where tall pine trees stood in quiet meditation, hiding the moon from sight.

'I don't see the moon,' she said, when he stopped walking.

He traced a finger down her nose and around her lips. 'You wouldn't see it anyway if you closed your eyes,' he whispered. His face came closer and his mouth found hers before she could say another word. He kissed her with a soft sensuality that stirred every nerve in her body. Her arms slipped around him and he drew her very close, her breast pressing against his chest. She responded recklessly and she knew there was a danger there and she didn't care. Her heart raced. Reid was an expert kisser, that much she already knew. There had been other men in her life who had been expert kissers, but not quite like this, not quite like Mr Reid McShane. Why was she feeling like this? Senseless, mindless, careless . . . oh, don't go bananas over a kiss, she thought angrily. And then she couldn't think any more—not a thought, not a word . . .

She tore herself away. Good lord, a single kiss and she was devastated! She began to walk away through the trees. Reid followed her.

'Hey,' he said, 'did I do something wrong?' He sounded wounded.

'No, you did it very well. Too well, actually.' He disturbed her. Her feelings disturbed her. She felt threatened. This was not the time for her to have a love affair.

So, she said to herself, why then did you come here?

He groaned. 'All I did was kiss you.'

'Some kiss!'

He sighed theatrically. 'Yeah, shattering, isn't it? It always gets me into trouble. One little kiss and . . .'

'Oh, shut up!'

He laughed out loud, and then Beth started laughing too; she couldn't help herself. She ran back around the house, across the pasture to the pond, and Reid ran after her. Breathing hard, they stood together on the dock, facing each other.

'I'm going to kiss you again,' he whispered.

'Look!' she pointed at random, diverting his attention intentionally.

He looked. And at that precise moment she gave him a shove with all her might and he lost his balance and plunged sideways into the water.

He came up spluttering almost immediately.

'That'll teach you!' she called, and began to run for her life. Out of breath she reached the house, realising suddenly that he wasn't following her at all. Feeling like a fool, she opened the door and went in.

Now what? Should she wait in the living room, or lock herself in her bedroom?

Lock herself in the bedroom, definitely. She did, turned off the light and sat on the bed, silent as a mouse.

She waited. The house was very quiet. She waited some more. Not a sound. This was not funny any more. Was Reid biding his time to see if she'd come out looking for him? Was he hiding outside the door, ready to pounce on her? Was this his revenge? Funny, funny.

No, it wasn't. She got up from the bed, unlocked the bedroom door and crept silently to the front door. Opening it a crack, she listened. A strange sound reached her ears, like a muffled curse. Movement caught her eyes, a hunched-over apparition in the dark.

Reid. She opened up the door wider and saw him limping up the path.

'Come and help me!' He sounded angry—definitely very, very angry. With a sinking feeling in her chest Beth ran to his aid, and together they struggled inside. In the kitchen he sat down on a chair, his face twisting in pain. There was no need to ask what had happened. He had sprained his left ankle, or worse, broken it. Without a word Beth knelt down in front of him and eased off his shoe and sock as carefully as possible. Not carefully enough, though, gathering from his groaned expletives. The foot was badly swollen.

'I'll get some ice.'

She dumped a tray of ice cubes into a plastic bag, wrapped a dish towel around it and draped the affair as well as she could around his ankle.

Reid hadn't said a word to her, and now she sat down with a sigh and looked at him. He was watching her, face grim.

'I'm sorry.' She didn't know what else to say. She felt terrible. 'Does it hurt a lot?'

'Enough.'

'Maybe it's broken. Maybe I'd better take you to the emergency room for X-rays, just to be sure.' Oh, lord, the hospital was twenty miles away and Josh was in bed asleep. They couldn't leave him. And Grandma Daisy was probably asleep too at this time of night.

'It's just a sprain. I've had enough of them to know.' He twisted in his chair and swore. 'I'll see how it is tomorrow.'

Had he not been in pain, it would have been funny. Soaking wet, his shirt clung to him. His hair glistened with drops of water that ran down his forehead and dripped from his chin. Greenish black waterweeds clung to his shoulder and he was a sorry sight. He wiped at his face and gave her a furious look.

'How about a towel?'

Jumping up, she almost tripped over her own feet.

'Calm down!' he growled impatiently. 'One invalid in the house is enough.'

In normal circumstances she wouldn't have ignored his tone of voice, would probably have told him to go jump in the lake or take a hike, neither of which would have been very appropriate at the moment. As it was, she felt overwhelmed with guilt. It was her fault he had hurt his ankle, indirectly at least.

When she came back with the towel he had taken off his shirt and it lay on the floor in a wet soggy heap next to his sports shoe and sock. He began rubbing his hair and face, then his bare chest. It was covered with the same dark curly hair that sat on his head. His eyes caught hers but held no humour.

'How about taking off my other shoe?' It was an order more than a question, but it didn't seem to matter. Beth bent down and pulled on the mucky shoelaces.

'How did it happen?' she asked.

'I tripped, what else.' He groaned between his teeth as he moved in the chair. 'It's too damned dark to race across the pasture at this time of night.'

'Then you shouldn't have.' It was the wrong thing to say, she realised immediately.

'Lady, you pushed me in the damned pond!'

'I didn't make you chase after me!' Why was she saying something stupid like that? She felt angry—at herself, at him, at what had happened. Why didn't she just shut up?

'Hah!'

There was a long silence. Reid watched her through narrowed eyes.

'Why the hell did you do that?' he demanded.

Defence, she wanted to say. You scare the hell out of me. She shrugged. 'I don't know,' she said instead.

He stared at her, eyes dark. 'You *accepted* my invitation for a stroll in the moonlight. What were you expecting?'

'A stroll in the moonlight.'

'Ah, such innocence! It melts my heart.'

Beth wasn't enjoying this. It would be easy enough to get vicious and nasty, but she didn't have the stomach for it right now. Here he was, Mr Handsome, mad, wet, and immobilised, and it wasn't even funny. She looked at his bare foot covered with the ice pack, the wet jeans.

'You should get out of those wet pants,' she said tonelessly.

'Yeah, you want to help me?' His tone was sarcastic. He wasn't making it easy for her, was he?

'Sure,' she shrugged, unconcerned.

'Like hell you will! Go to my room and get me my bathrobe. It's behind the door.'

Anger really surfaced now. 'Listen here, mister! If you want your damn bathrobe you can ask for it in a civilised manner and say please!'

There was a sudden unexpected flash of laughter in his eyes and his mouth twitched almost indiscernibly. 'Would you please get me my bathrobe? It's behind my bedroom door.'

Turning her back, she marched out of the kitchen and did as he requested.

'I'll turn my back while you change. I'll fix you a drink.'

'You get out of here!'

Groaning in exasperation, Beth walked out. 'And they say women are prudes!'

One swift movement of his left arm and the next thing she knew his wet shirt, slithery strands of water-weeds and all, was draped over her head and in front of her face.

It was such a total surprise that for a moment she was bereft of speech. Tearing the wet mass from her face, she felt anger race through her, and then she saw his face . . . the big grin, full of malicious satisfaction.

'That'll teach you,' he said softly.

She stared at him hard, not saying a word, then turned slowly and retreated in as dignified a manner as she was capable of. Reid's laughter followed her.

Ten minutes later, cooled down, she ventured back into the kitchen. Bathrobe on, he sat slumped in the chair. The ice had fallen off his foot, and it shocked her to see his ankle. It looked worse than any sprain she'd ever seen. It was so badly swollen, so purple and blue and black, it frightened her. What if it were broken?

'Let me help you to the living room,' she offered. 'You'll be more comfortable on the sofa.'

'I'll be more comfortable yet in my bed,' he said dryly.

They managed to get there, somehow, and with a sigh of relief Reid lay back on the pillow. His bed was large and looked comfortable, a contemporary design with a shelving unit built into the headboard. There were books, magazines and a reading lamp. The floor was covered with soft cream carpeting and besides an easy chair, a husky antique dresser was the only furniture. It was a restful, peaceful room without pretence. Beth looked back at Reid, finding him watching her.

'There's an elastic bandage somewhere,' he said, and told her where to look. At his instructions she wound it around his ankle after she'd first put a cushion under his leg. After that she arranged the ice around his foot once more, then straightening, she studied his face. His eyes were closed. He looked pale and by the grim set of his mouth she knew he was in pain.

'Shall I get you some aspirin?' she asked.

He opened his eyes. 'I'd rather have a drink. A double Scotch on the rocks, please.'

She swallowed hard. 'I didn't mean for this to happen,' she said miserably. 'I'm sorry—I feel terrible.'

He smiled faintly and it smoothed out the lines of his face, making him look slightly better. 'I'm sorry I lost my temper. I'll be all right, don't worry. And I'm not angry at you. You know, sometimes when people play games, people get hurt.'

The alarm clock woke her at three in the morning, and groggy with sleep, she dragged herself out of bed. In the kitchen she made another ice pack and then slipped into Reid's room as quietly as she could. She heard him stir.

'Beth?'

'Yes. I have some more ice for you. Have you been awake long?'

He switched on the bedside lamp. 'Off and on. Every time I move I go through the ceiling. It tends to wake me up.'

His foot lay still elevated on the small pillow, but the ice had slipped off and was mostly water now. Beth took it away and draped the fresh ice pack around his foot as securely as possible. She saw him wince and he grimaced apologetically.

'I'm sorry I'm being such a baby, but it does hurt like hell.'

Beth would have been surprised if it hadn't. She remembered how it had looked in the kitchen—the terrible swelling, the awful colours.

'Men are allowed to show pain, it's a new law.'

He grinned. 'About time too. It's been hard being tough and macho all these years. What about aspirin? Are we allowed that without losing face?'

'Aspirin too. Shall I get you some?'

'Please. You're too kind.'

'I know.' She left to get a glass of water and some aspirin.

He gulped them down and drained the glass. 'Were you awake, or was this a special mission to minister to me at this hour of the night?'

'A special mission. I knew your ice wasn't going to last, and I know it's important to keep your ankle cold to keep the swelling down. It was bad enough to start with.'

She was sitting cross-legged on the soft carpeting waiting for him to finish, thinking how strange it was for her to be sitting here in his bedroom in the middle of the night. There were ads in magazines of men and women sensuously draped on velvety carpeting, drinking golden wine in golden light. Silky-stockinged legs were stretched out seductively while silvery strapped high heels lay abandoned nearby. Sometimes the picture sported a candle, sometimes a single red rose, sometimes both. In the background there was invariably a double bed with the most luxurious and romantic linens.

Beth trailed her fingers through the carpeting, feeling its soft, luxurious thickness. So far so good. She was sitting on it, but not draped out on it. She could try sticking out one leg, but lacking a silky stocking it probably wouldn't look quite the same. Not that there was anything wrong with her legs; she'd even freshly polished her toenails last night. Her bathrobe was only tied in the middle—she could let it slide off her legs to her hips if she wanted to. No wine glasses, although Reid had his water glass, which he'd put on the floor next to his bed. No rose, no candles. No sensational long curly hair either for her. What else was missing? Ah, the man, the sensuous, sensitive man looking at the woman in romantic adoration. The man available lay crashed on the rumpled bed with his eyes closed and his foot wrapped in ice.

Well, you can't have everything, she thought.

For a while she sat quietly, watching him. He had a wonderful face—strong, masculine, without looking hard and ruthless. There was usually warmth in his eyes and a sensitive expression, especially when he was with Josh. Beth grinned to herself. Whoop-de-do! A man with a heart.

Reid opened his eyes unexpectedly and let them rest on her face. With his right hand he patted the empty space next to him. 'Don't just sit there. Crawl in.'

The invitation was a surprise, but she recovered quickly. 'The aspirin is starting to work, is it?'

His eyes were laughing. 'Mmmm . . . some. Not enough. You'll be safe, though. I have no designs on your body. Correction—any designs I have on your body are doomed. I'm not in a position to carry them through. I am absolutely and completely incapacitated . . . more or less.'

'You're lecherous, and thank you for the nice invitation, but I'd better sleep in my own bed. Safer for you. I kick a lot in my sleep.'

She walked out, hearing his low laugh, then a frustrated groan of pain.

Next morning Reid tried and failed to stand on his foot, which was a ridiculous albeit courageous effort in Beth's opinion. His face contracted with pain. 'Damn, damn!' he swore. 'Do me a favour, Beth, and get me some crutches from Daisy. I think she has some lying around from last summer when her grandson was with her and broke his leg.'

He struggled around on the crutches, but kept his foot up most of the day, lying on the sofa reading some gory-looking novel.

It was Beth who did most of the chores around the house. She milked the goat and fed the chickens and gathered the eggs and picked an endless supply of green beans and raspberries. She was paying for pushing him in the pond, that was for sure. She more or less took over the entire household in the next few days.

People came and went, mostly two men who parked themselves near the sofa and talked business with Reid while she fed them coffee and cake or drinks and cheese and crackers. They talked about the housing project and were always too deep in discussion to take much notice of her. She wasn't sure how she felt about that. Maybe wearing her working uniform of old jeans and a faded T-shirt had something to do with that. Sitting in the kitchen one morning, she was giving the matter some low key, idle thought, her hands busy cutting green beans into a big bowl on her lap, feet supported on a rung of a chair in front of her.

If Jack could see me now, she thought, he'd have a fit. The things he would say to her were in her mind already. She grinned at the thought.

The beans were almost done, thank God. Now she'd have to embark on the adventure of boiling and freezing them.

Reid limped into the kitchen on one leg and one crutch. An empty coffee cup dangled from a finger of his free hand.

'Take those beans to Daisy,' he ordered. 'She said she'd do them.'

'I'd like to try it myself, if you don't mind.'

'Don't you have enough to do?'

She shrugged. 'I don't mind working. This is all new to me. Make yourself comfortable and give me instructions.' She waved at a chair, smiling airily.

Reid struggled into a chair. 'You make it sound like some gigantic undertaking. There isn't much to it.'

'There isn't much to casting bait, either,' she returned, grinning.

He laughed. 'I admire your interest for the new and untried.'

Inclining her head, she smiled graciously. 'Thank yah, sah,' she said in her best southern drawl, which was atrocious.

Josh came in, dragging his feet, drank down a glass of orange juice and departed again without as much as a look or word at either of them. Reid's eyes followed him, bushy eyebrows frowning.

Josh wasn't happy with his father being incapacitated. He wasn't happy with Beth either. He didn't like the way she was taking over; it was obvious in his attitude and in everything he said. His eyes and face radiated displeasure.

It was obvious to Beth that Reid had noticed Josh's behaviour for some time, but so far he had made no comment.

After he had put Josh to bed that night, Reid hobbled into the kitchen where Beth was cleaning up after a late dinner.

'Do you have any idea what's the matter with him?' he asked brusquely. 'I tried, but I can't get a word out of him.'

She was cleaning the counter, wiping up some spilled mashed potatoes. Raising her head, she met his eyes. There was anger there, and worry and frustration.

'He doesn't like me. He doesn't want me around, mostly. Is he like that with all women?'

Reid frowned and ran an impatient hand through his bushy hair. 'He hasn't been around them much on a long-term basis. We've stayed with my sister and her family in Florida for a week or so, now and then. Never any problem there.' He shrugged. 'He loves Daisy.'

Beth wiped carefully around the burners on the stove, mopping up gravy spills, drops of cooking water, a solitary pea. 'She's sixty-eight and lives down the road.'

There was a pause. She could almost feel him thinking.

'And you're twenty-six and staying here.'

'Right in his own house.' Without looking at him she crossed to the sink and ran the hot water to rinse out the sponge, then put it down and faced him.

'He feels threatened, Reid, for one reason or another. And it's worse now because I do more.'

He sighed heavily. 'Well, whatever the reason, I don't like the way he's been acting lately.'

'I'm not crazy about it myself,' she said dryly. For a moment she hesitated. 'He said something about his mother having to go right after he was born. I don't want to sound like Freud, but maybe he doesn't like me because I'm a mother-type. As far as he can tell, I fit the description.'

She could say more, but didn't. The idea was clear enough. Maybe Josh hated his mother for leaving him. Maybe that was why he didn't want anything to do with Beth, either. Or maybe he was waiting for her to come back, and in the meantime nobody was going to take her place if he could help it. It was all speculation. There was no way to understand it without knowing all the background.

Reid looked thoughtful, rubbing fists together as if that could help him think. 'I hadn't thought about that, but it seems credible enough.' He looked at her directly. 'I know it isn't anything you've done. I never thought that. Please don't think that.' The expression in his eyes made her heart do a somersault and the words settled inside her, warm and glowing.

'I know. I don't.'

'I don't imagine he has any great love for a mother he's never seen. I've tried to keep my own negative feelings out of it when I explain the situation to him, but God knows it's not easy.' He stared off into space, lost in memories. Not happy ones, she could see from the hard look on his face.

'Are you divorced?' The question was out before she could check herself.

His eyes came back to her face while he slowly shook his head. 'No, his mother and I were never married.'

It wasn't really what she had expected, although she'd realised it could have been anything. It did leave her feeling a little awkward because she had no idea how to respond to that.

'Are you shocked?' He looked at her, faintly amused.

'No ... it's just not what I had expected. Shock doesn't come to me that easily. I've been around for a while.'

He gave a low laugh and studied her face with speculation.

'Make us a drink while I transport myself to the sofa, and then I'll tell you the whole sorry tale.'

CHAPTER THREE

BETH'S hands moved automatically as she took out glasses, ice, a bottle of Scotch and another of vodka, putting them all on the counter that separated the kitchen from the living room. It was well designed, that counter. It could serve as a breakfast table, a bar, and it could be used for buffet dinners. Beth gazed at the arrangement of glasses and bottles in front of her. Right—Scotch on the rocks for Reid, vodka and orange juice for herself.

So Josh was an illegitimate child, as the law called it so melodramatically—as if it were against the law for him to exist, to live, to breathe. She splashed Scotch over the ice in Reid's glass. He never bothered with a shot glass, so she wouldn't either.

Illegitimate. Born out of wedlock. Good lord, it was almost funny! The words conjured up all manner of associations that had nothing to do with Reid. Josh, an illegitimate child. Well, there were more than a few around these days, and nobody was shocked any more.

She poured vodka into her glass, replaced the bottle in the cabinet and found a carton of orange juice in the refrigerator.

So what had happened? Had Reid impregnated some romantic teenager? Had he been forced to take care of the child? Ridiculous. Maybe he'd had a fling with a woman his own age and refused to marry her. No, not that either. It couldn't be. A woman his own age wouldn't have got herself pregnant, and if she had she

53

would have taken care of the situation herself, one way
or another.

Something was different here. Something didn't
click. In the lives of illegitimate children the fathers
were usually obviously and permanently absent. Not so
for Josh. She'd never seen a father and son so close.
It was his mother who 'had to go away,' as Josh had
said himself. The memory of that conversation was still
clear in her mind.

She replaced the orange juice in the refrigerator and
put the drinks on a small tray.

Maybe Josh wasn't really Reid's son. The thought
was like a shock. Maybe he had taken him because a
younger sister, or . . .

Well, she was about to find out. She carried the tray
into the living room, put it on the coffee table and
handed Reid his glass. He smiled at her and suddenly
she felt a cold nervousness come over her.

It wasn't any of her business, but she wanted to
know. She really wanted to know. She was afraid to
know, too, she couldn't tell why. Yes, she did. She
didn't want to know anything about him that would
give her any negative feelings.

Nobody's perfect, she thought wildly. We all have
our dirty little secrets, Mr Wonderful as well as everybody else.

But I don't want to know his, she thought miserably.
Please, Reid, you're one of the good ones, don't tell
me something I don't want to know.

She curled up in the roomy overstuffed chair she'd
made her own. Good for reading, watching TV, thinking, listening. She took a sip from her drink.

One of the good ones. What had made her think
that? Because Doc had praised him to the sky? No, oh
no. It had helped, she supposed, but it was a feeling,

an instinct, and she didn't want it shattered. Heavens, she thought, you're neurotic. The man is human. What do you want him to be? A saint?

Reid shifted restlessly on the sofa as if he couldn't get quite comfortable. It was obvious his ankle was still hurting him. It could take months before it would be normal again, he had said glumly. Sometimes a clean break healed faster than a sprain. Was she going to have to feel guilty for ever?

He took a big swallow of his drink, then rested the glass on his stomach.

'You look worried,' he commented.

'I'm not. Just thinking serious thoughts.' She grinned a little, then looked down into her glass and examined the melting ice cubes.

'Reid,' she said after a pause, 'is Josh really your son?' Meeting his eyes, she saw his surprise.

'Genes, blood and all. Why?'

'I don't know, really. I was wondering.'

'His mother didn't want him.' His voice was hard. 'It's the gist of the whole story. She didn't want him and I did.' He lifted his glass and had another sip. 'His mother and I lived together for two years. We were both very much involved in our careers, working crazy hours with not much time for fun and games. We were in the same boat, so to speak. We understood each other. It was a very comfortable relationship for both of us, until things went wrong.' He paused for a while as if he didn't quite know where to go on from there.

Beth didn't know what to say. She examined her nails. They looked terrible. She should stop digging around in the garden, she thought stupidly. What did she care about her nails right now?

'She's a biologist,' Reid went on. 'Quite brilliant. She was working under some famous researcher. I admired her for her brains. She had a very rational, logical mind. She had the ability to analyse a problem in no time at all, make up her mind about its solution and then stick with it.' He looked at her wryly. 'It was these same characteristics that led to my current status as an unmarried father.' He finished his drink in one great gulp.

Beth was silent. She studied him, seeing the tightness in his face, his jawline hard, his mouth drawn back a little. He was not enjoying this story and heaven knew why he was doing this to himself. 'You don't have to tell me anything, if you'd rather not. It's . . .'

He shrugged. 'I've started, I'll finish.'

Knees pulled up under her chin, she waited, but nothing came. She wished he would look at her; it made her uneasy to see him so silent and thoughtful. She bit her lower lip and rubbed her bare feet together. The nail gloss on her toes shone darkly in the light.

'What's her name?' she asked after a while.

Reid glanced at her quickly. 'Carol.'

Carol. The name alone conjured up no particular type of woman. Could be short and blonde or tall and dark, or anything in between. She'd known several Carols in her life, all different types. Like the different Marys or Sues she'd had among her friends and relatives.

Carol. She thought of Josh, looked at Reid. This one was probably a tall brunette with brown eyes and glasses with big, fashionable designer frames and lots of thick wavy brown hair down to her shoulders. Inadvertently she touched her own short cap of hair, smooth and straight. A super cut, short and easy. It suited her. She wished it were shoulder-length and wavy. Why was she thinking such stupid, frivolous, irrelevant thoughts.

'She got pregnant,' Reid said at last. 'It was unplanned and unexpected. First she was shocked, then she went into a rage. She didn't want a kid to keep her from working, from building her career. She never really wanted children at all. They didn't fit in with her life style or her plans.

'She decided to have an abortion. She decided that without even asking me what *I* wanted, without ever discussing her feelings with me. She presented me with a final decision.' He looked at Beth for a moment, and it shocked her to see so much anger and bitterness in his eyes.

'I have never, never been so angry in my life,' he said in a low voice. 'It was the turning point of our relationship. Planned or unplanned, this baby was mine as well as hers, and at the very least she could have had the courtesy of involving me in making a decision regarding the future.

'I told her I wanted the baby. I didn't like the idea of having it "taken care of" because it was "inconvenient". Between the two of us there were plenty of options. We were not desperate in any real way. We were mature adults, both professionals. I'll never forget the way she looked at me, as if she hated me. "You want the baby?" she asked. "Okay, you carry it." ' He closed his eyes. 'God, it was an ugly fight!'

She could imagine. A shiver went through her. She could practically see the two of them facing each other, both furious and frightened. She could almost hear them speaking. Her mind was always doing this to her, making true life out of anything that passed through it—words, thoughts, images, all in Technicolor brilliance. It was part of the reason for her success and she knew it. Sometimes she wished she could slow down the creative processes, or send them on vacation, something.

What would I do? she asked herself. What if I were in the middle of a blossoming career ... (but I am, I am!). What would I do if I got pregnant? How could she ever honestly answer that without being in the position? It was so easy to judge other people, standing on the sidelines. She drank the rest of her drink and swirled around the melting ice cubes, making them clink against the side of the glass.

'It must have been terrible,' she said. 'For both of you. What happened?'

The corner of his mouth pulled down in a humourless smile. 'I called my lawyer. Actually he was and is a good friend. He didn't deal with cases like mine, but he got hold of one of his friends who did. The two of them came to see us pronto, that night, believe it or not. We sat around for hours discussing the situation. All that time she sat there in a chair, chain-smoking, not saying a damned word unless asked a question.' He laughed grimly. 'I can tell you, expectant fathers don't have a helluva lot of rights if they're not married to the expectant mothers. And marriage was no solution. It had never been in the plans; we didn't have that kind of relationship. She said flat out she didn't want to marry because of the child. She wasn't going to have it—period.

'So the men of law and justice departed, and I knew that she could walk out the door in the morning and come back that night and there would be no more baby. There was nothing I could do to prevent her from doing it.'

There was a long silence. He was very tense, as if just the memory of it all brought back the initial emotions all over again. He was rubbing the knuckles of his clenched hands together in an unconscious gesture of concentration. Beth had seen him do it on other occasions—a small habit she'd started to recognise, just as his habit of always getting down on his haunches when he spoke sternly to his son. Never would he stand up and tower over him, spewing his anger down from great heights. Other things—the way he scraped butter off the top of the bar rather than cutting a slice off the end. The observer of things and people, she thought dryly. Part of the job too. You could never tell what might be used in a deodorant commercial one day.

'I need another drink,' he said suddenly. Beth jumped up and reached for his empty glass. She made herself another screwdriver, going easy on the vodka. This was not the time to overdo it with the drink and say stupid things, or laugh at the wrong time.

Reid had shifted his position when she came back into the room. Sitting up more or less straight, he had put his injured foot on a cushion on the floor.

'Thanks,' he said as she handed him his glass. 'You make a wonderful servant.'

'A good thing my father couldn't hear that. He intended for me to *have* servants.'

Looking right at her, Reid slowly shook his head. 'Oh, you and your father . . .' he said meaningfully.

'We weren't talking about me,' she said quickly, taking a gulp from her drink.

'No.' He studied her face for a moment. 'What are you thinking?'

'I . . . I was wondering why you wanted that baby so much.'

He smiled a little now, and it made her feel better. He bent over and put his glass on the table.

'When she told me my first reaction was disbelief. I'd never considered the possibility. According to the statistics our chances of her getting pregnant were practically nil. But then, when I realised that what she was telling me was real and true, I . . .' he smiled faintly, 'I can't begin to describe my feelings. I was totally overwhelmed by it. There was this baby growing inside her—*my* child, *my* girl or *my* boy, and I . . . I was delirious, ecstatic, totally and completely out of my mind with joy.'

He paused, eyes suddenly dark and the smile gone. 'And then she told me she didn't want it, that she was going to have an abortion. God, it's a good thing I'm not a violent man, or I don't know what I would have done.'

'But she did have the baby, Reid,' she said softly. 'What happened?'

A strange look came into his face. 'After my lawyer friend had left with his friend we were alone again. I remember sitting there watching her smoking one cigarette after another, silent, not looking at me. I remember thinking she shouldn't be smoking like that, how bad it was for the baby, and that she didn't care. Never before had I felt so totally helpless, and never in my life had anything mattered so much to me. I . . . I started bawling like a kid out of sheer frustration.' He smiled ruefully. 'Ever seen a grown man cry?'

'No.'

'Are you shocked?'

'No. There's a new law that says . . .'

'Whose law?'

'Mine.'

He laughed. 'Somehow I'm not surprised.' For a fleeting moment there was something in his expression that made her heart double its speed. Then he glanced away, his thoughts turned inward again.

'She started crying too,' he said at last, his voice very low. 'She sat all curled up in her chair, her head on her knees . . . miserable. The most awful thing of it all,' he said slowly, 'was that we couldn't comfort each other. I realised then how very much apart we really were, had always been. Our relationship had no real foundation, it collapsed as soon as a crisis confronted it. We couldn't pull together and weather it somehow as a team.

'We went to bed, separately, saying not a word to each other. We had breakfast in silence. She left at her usual time, came back that night, mixed herself a drink and told me—without looking at me—that she would have the baby if I really wanted it. I'd gone through hell all night and all day. I didn't know if I was dreaming or going crazy or what. I must have looked like a loony staring at her, and then I wanted to . . .' He stopped for a moment, as if it was hard to speak. 'I wanted to take her in my arms and tell her we'd manage, that I'd take care of her. I wanted somehow to make this dreadful tension between us go away. But she didn't give me a chance. She pushed me away and looked at me as if I were a madman.

' "I'm not finished," she said. "I'll have the baby on the condition that you will take on the sole responsibility for its welfare and upbringing. I don't want to be involved in any circumstances." Cold as the arctic, the lady was. Her entire personality had changed. I didn't recognise her any more.'

'Why did she change her mind about having the baby?' asked Beth.

'I have no idea. She didn't want to talk any more. To her the subject was closed. Our whole life changed after that.'

'Sounds like a nightmare to me,' said Beth, giving an involuntary shiver.

'You could say that,' Reid agreed dryly. 'We stayed together until the baby was born. I don't know if that was good or bad, but it's a moot point now. She breezed through her pregnancy as if it were nothing. She took good care of herself, stopped smoking cold turkey, only had an occasional drink. She wasn't sick a day, didn't miss a day of work until she took her maternity leave.'

He looked at Beth, eyes dark. 'I felt guilty as hell, I really don't know why. Somehow, somewhere, I'd failed her. I had no real explanations. I kept thinking maybe I'd been too selfish, I was asking too much of her. I tried to talk to her, but she didn't want to. I couldn't reach her at all. She locked everything up and she wasn't letting me in. Those months, those endless months . . . they were hell. We had no relationship to speak of, we hardly talked to each other except for the normal daily civilities. We were strangers.'

'Did she not mind people seeing her pregnant, knowing she would never have the baby to show for it afterwards?'

He shrugged. 'I doubt it. She wasn't bothered by what other people thought of her. Cool as a cucumber, the lady was. Hard as a block of concrete is more like it, probably.'

Beth didn't like that.

'What's the matter?' asked Reid, looking at her.

'I don't like the way you talk about her.' Good heavens, who was she to judge? She didn't even know the woman.

He frowned. 'How am I supposed to talk about her? With love and compassion? I tried everything I could to save the situation. And she did all she could to make my life miserable. She was making me pay. She was making me pay, Beth, and those months were the worst in my life.'

How could she ever try to understand the motivations of another person? How could she ever know the feelings and emotions of someone else when she'd never been in the same situation?

'How old was she when she got pregnant?' she asked.

'Twenty-seven.'

Only one year older than I am now, Beth thought.

'And right in the middle of getting somewhere professionally, right?'

'Right.'

'Don't you understand how difficult that is? Women are supposed to be able to do it all—have kids, a career. It doesn't work very well in a lot of cases. You make her seem inhuman. If she'd really been that hard and unfeeling she wouldn't have gone through with her pregnancy. You wanted the baby and she gave it to you. You owe her that. It was probably the most difficult and courageous thing she ever did. She must have felt terribly lonely.'

Why am I saying this? What do I know? Sisterhood, she thought. That's it. Sisterhood.

Reid looked at her with surprise, then waved his hand in a helpless gesture. 'You may well be right. I can't be objective about it, I know. I wanted that baby so badly I couldn't imagine she didn't. I could rationalise it, but I couldn't *feel* it. After my initial disbelief, something happened to me. It became terribly real. Nothing else seemed more important at that moment. I had visions of myself taking my kid to the circus, to the beach. I was ready to buy out the toy store.' He gave a crooked little grin and shook his head at his own premature enthusiasm. 'Given the circumstances I was truly insane.'

Beth wasn't so sure about that. After all, he was

talking about his own baby, wasn't he? Married or not, he was the father.

His words had the strangest effect on her. She'd watched him as he talked and he was watching her too, and suddenly he grinned.

'You're going all soft and sentimental,' he said. 'You should see your face.'

She wanted to hit him. Colour crept into her face and his grin widened.

For a long moment she looked at him silently.

'I've heard a lot of bitter tales of women who were abandoned by the men who fathered their children, who wanted nothing to do with them. It's good to hear the enthusiasm of a father for once.'

'I'm not a saint,' he said. 'A perfect father, yes, but not a saint.'

'Who said you are?' she asked coolly.

'You looked at me very adoringly.'

'You suffer from an inflated ego. I've never *adored* anybody in my life.'

'The idea a bit too servile for you?' he queried.

'You bet!'

'How about getting some cheese and crackers? I'm hungry.' He gave the most charming smile and Beth couldn't help laughing.

'You know how to get me, don't you?'

'I try, I try.'

He would be able to get to the kitchen himself, but carrying the stuff back all in one hand was asking for trouble. There was no other way but for her to do it.

'So,' she said after she sat down again, 'what did you do after Josh was born?'

'It was all very well organised, like a damn business transaction. She'd found herself an apartment, furnished it and had it all ready. It was agreed that I would take the baby home with me and she would go to her new apartment and go on with her life from there.' He paused for a moment, as if not sure how to go on.

'When the baby was born,' he continued then, 'I went into her room to say goodbye. I didn't know what to say exactly and I got out something about the baby being beautiful and that I was happy and would take good care of him. She started to cry. It was the only time I ever saw her cry after that first awful night.'

'She may have cried a lot while you weren't looking.'

'Maybe. I never saw her again after that. She never came to my place, she never even called. I don't even know where she is now. I keep looking at Josh and I can't forgive her for not wanting him, I can't forgive her for not wanting to be his mother.'

Beth watched him, a lump in her throat. He was looking into his glass and she saw the faint trembling of his hand.

It was so strange sitting here, listening to him, watching him. All through his story he never called Josh's mother by her name, referred to her only as 'she'. Josh's mother now was only a stranger, an undefined 'she'. There was a lot of unresolved bitterness still lingering.

He began to talk again, telling her he had bought all the necessities with the help of a friend and his wife and had stored them in their house until he could bring the baby home. Slowly his face relaxed as he began to tell her about those first few weeks as a new father, and a smile came into his face and lit up his eyes.

'I didn't think I was going to survive, let alone the poor kid.'

'Didn't you have anyone to help you? Did you take

him home alone?' Beth was so surprised, she was laughing.

'You mean a nanny, or some other female?' There was challenging laughter in his eyes now. 'No, my dear Beth, I did not. Nobody was coming close to my kid. In the hospital I'd been given elaborate instructions from the nurses. They demonstrated and let me practise under their supervision. They were a great help. They also told me there was no reason why I couldn't do as well as any new mother, so off I went. The pediatrician was a great help too, and in my apartment building there were lots of mothers with babies, and in time of crisis I could call on them.'

Beth laughed. 'Wow! So you did it all, mixing formulas, changing diapers, everything.'

'Everything.'

'What about your job? Didn't you work?'

'Didn't I work?' he asked slowly, very slowly, and she knew she'd made a mistake. 'I *slaved*! Over a hot stove, in the laundry room, in the morning, afternoon and night. Ever heard of two o'clock feedings?'

Beth couldn't help laughing. 'Touché! But you know what I mean.'

'I took leave of absence, then decided I wanted to work on my own and quit. I wanted to build this house. I didn't really want to go back to work full time because I wanted to spend time with Josh, and I didn't want to get back in the rat race, and there were some other reasons—so here I am.'

'You had to eat, too,' she reminded him.

'True, but I knew I wouldn't go hungry.'

'You're lucky. Life becomes a lot easier when you don't have to worry where your next meal is coming from. Don't let anyone kid you about the nobility of poverty.'

Reid raised his eyebrows. 'You know about that?'

She shook her head. 'No, but I read that somewhere, and it sounds good.'

He gave a hearty laugh.

'How did you manage to build a house with him so small?' asked Beth.

'Lived in a trailer on the site. I started in the spring. I had a big playpen and for the first few months he was quite happy watching me and playing around. When he started crawling it became too much of a problem to keep him from swallowing nails and bolts . . .'

'. . . electric wire, plumbing pipe, cabinet knobs . . .'

'Exactly,' he said, face deadpan. 'I hired a teenage girl during the summer months to keep him out of trouble while I was busy. I bought a sandbox and a wading pool and that kept him entertained quite well. By the time it was winter we could move in, although there was still a lot of work to be done. He could walk by then and I had to be careful, but I managed.'

He told her about the house, how he had built it with some outside help from a plumber and an electrician who thought he was crazy to build a 'cave', and about the trouble he'd had with the inspector who came out to look over the place and see if it adhered to the local building codes.

The second summer he'd built the storage shed, the hen house and the goat shelter with the lumber from an old, fallen-down barn that had been on the property when he'd bought it. He'd started a garden, which was a total disaster the first year, and he'd stocked the pond with bass.

'Grandma Daisy came over regularly to give me advice on gardens and babies and country living.' He grinned. 'She didn't think much of me at first, and she made very, very sure I was treating that baby right.

She brought me homemade bread and apples and tomatoes and she offered to babysit for Josh any time I had to go somewhere. Now there was a helpful lady.'

He lapsed into silence.

It had grown dark outside and they had been sitting in the half-light that flooded over from the kitchen. Beth got up to turn on the lights, feeling his eyes on her as she moved around the room. She felt nervous and didn't know why. Or did she?

Reid reached for her as she switched on the reading lamp next to the sofa.

'Beth?'

His hand was holding her hand and her heart made a ridiculous somersault. 'What?'

'What I've told you is very private and very personal, you know that, don't you?'

She nodded. 'Of course.'

His eyes held hers and it was happening again—the lightheadedness, the breathlessness, the tingling sensation going all through her.

A shine came into his eyes. 'Did you have to turn on every blasted light in the room? It's light enough in here to do micro-surgery!'

Beth said nothing. She stood in front of him like a statue, his hand warm around hers. She wanted to touch him, put her hands on his hair to feel its springy texture. She wanted to run her fingers gently down the lines of his face. All she had to do was go down on her knees to bring their faces level and reach out.

It was dangerously simple, but something withheld her and the seconds went by. Neither of them moved.

'Beth ...' he whispered, 'something is terribly wrong with me.'

'What?' The answer was automatic.

'I have this suicidal urge to kiss you.' He gave her

hand a gentle but unexpected tug and she lost her balance and flopped neatly next to him on the sofa. They were very close, but he didn't move, only looked at her. 'Maybe it's too dangerous,' he whispered.

'I can't push you in the water from here,' she whispered back.

'You might break my arm.'

She grinned. 'I don't think I'm strong enough for that.'

'Mmm . . . true.' His eyes didn't leave her face, and then, with maddening slowness, he leaned towards her. She closed her eyes as she felt his lips on her chin, her cheeks, her eyes, then slowly circling her mouth but not quite touching it. She felt a quivering sense of impatience and moved her mouth to find his, but he kept moving away, eluding her. Her heart beat wildly and a restless tension began to build. He was kissing her neck, her ear, then circling her mouth once more.

'Reid . . .' she whispered helplessly, 'don't!'

'Don't what? I'm not doing anything.' He bit her earlobe gently.

She squirmed in his arms. 'Don't tease me!'

'Mmm . . .' A soft, incoherent murmur came from his throat. He kissed the corner of her mouth, a touch so light she could barely feel it. Then there was the warmth of his tongue gently tracing her lips and the blood pounded in her ears. She pressed herself closer, parting her lips, and he was gone again.

'Reid . . . please . . .' She felt like a tightly wound coil ready to spring. How could he *do* this to her?

'What?' he murmured against her cheek.

'Kiss me properly, please . . .'

He relaxed his embrace, withdrawing slightly. He looked into her face and there was laughter in his eyes.

.'*Properly?*' he asked softly.

She took in a ragged breath. 'You're evil,' she said
vehemently.

He grinned. 'I know.' He drew her close again, and
with one swift movement of both his arms he slid her
across his thighs and on to his lap. One arm came
around her shoulders, the hand of the other lifted her
face to his. A smile touched his lips. 'Be prepared,' he
whispered. 'I'm going to kiss you properly . . . very,
very properly . . .'

Her heart leaped into her throat and she felt a
quivering of anticipation. She closed her eyes and put
her arms around his neck. His mouth found hers,
brushing her lips gently, then covering them with a
sudden impatience, kissing her deeply, hungrily. There
was no teasing now. A weakness came over her and in
one magic moment she had lost all sense of time and
place, was aware only of pure emotion, knowing only
the sweet excitement of his kiss and the sensuous
caresses of his wandering hand—such a big, strong and
infinitely gentle hand.

His breathing became more rapid and he murmured something unintelligible against her lips.
She kissed him with a feverish yearning, one hand
grasping the rough, curly hair at the back of his
head.

As by instinct they drew back at the same time. They
stared at each other, breathing hard. There was a sense
of hesitation, a sense of something new that needed to
be acknowledged.

Feeling suddenly much too close, Beth slid off his
lap and sat down again on the sofa, next to him, but
not too close. She stared hard at a book that lay on the
table. It was one of Josh's, with pictures of colourful
birds on its cover.

'You're having a disastrous effect on me,' he said

huskily. 'I'm beginning to lose my head. You'd better get out of here.'

She turned her head slowly and looked at him. 'I'll pack in the morning,' she whispered, having recovered.

'Don't you dare!' Reid grinned. 'It's not *that* disastrous!'

Beth laughed. 'I'll get out of reaching distance, then.' She got to her feet and as she moved away the phone rang. She picked up the extension in the kitchen.

'Hello?'

'Gotcha!'

Beth let out a deep sigh. 'Is that you, Jack?'

'Certainly is, sweetheart. How are you doing?'

'I was doing very well until a minute ago.' Reid was sitting right in her line of vision and she caught his grin. She turned her back on him. 'How did you get my number?'

'Somebody in Hong Kong told me.'

'What do you want, Jack?' She could feel herself grow angrier and angrier. He had found her number and she didn't like it one bit.

'I want *you*, darling,' he said.

She gritted her teeth. 'I'm not available!' She slammed the phone down and turned around, legs shaking.

'Sounds very encouraging to me,' said Reid. 'Boyfriend pining for you?'

'Oh, don't you start! That was my *boss* pining for me. If ever you get him on the line—Jack Coolidge is his name—tell him I'm not here, please.'

The phone rang.

'I'll get it.' He took his crutch and limped to the phone. 'Hello? Who?' He grinned at Beth. 'Beth Anderson, you said? Sorry, you must have the wrong number.' He replaced the receiver and leaned against the wall, waiting. Seconds later the phone rang again. Grinning, Reid went through the little charade once more.

'I don't think he'll call back again tonight. He sounded half-crocked.'

He was right. It remained silent after that.

'He wants me to come back to work,' Beth said tonelessly, feeling suddenly very tired, as if the thought alone drained her of energy. 'Doc told me to stay away two months if I could manage, but Jack doesn't seem to think it's necessary. Jack always knows better, of course.' There was bitterness in her voice. It was part of the problem at work—battles with Jack, too many battles with Jack. 'Anyway, I think it's time for bed.' She looked at him. 'Anything else I should do? I checked around outside earlier, everything seems fine.'

'You're getting to be quite a farm girl. Tomorrow we're going to freeze the beans. We can make tomato sauce and put it up if you're ready for that.'

She grinned, feeling better. 'I'm going to learn it all.'

She'd never frozen endless quarts of green beans, never made raspberry jam, never made yogurt, never baked bread. It was a different life, a different world, and she enjoyed it more than she'd ever thought possible. Grandma Daisy was a big help, teaching her the secrets of country living, sharing a wealth of knowledge gathered in sixty-odd years of living off the land. Grandma Daisy had had eight years of schooling, had raised five children, had never been farther from home than Richmond, not even to Washington, but her down-to-earth wisdom and knowledge staggered Beth, who soon added her to her list of favourite people.

The list was not very long, but Grandma Daisy belonged on it without a doubt.

Daisy had 'adopted' Reid and Josh as part of her family. 'He's a good man,' she said of Reid. 'I can tell by the eyes and the hands. You look, you'll see.'

Beth had already looked, and seen.

Reid's foot was much better now. He was walking on it again carefully, and it wouldn't be too long before even his limp would be gone. Jack had not called again, and she wondered if he really thought something was wrong with the number. Jack wasn't that stupid, though, she decided. He was biding his time.

Josh would soon start kindergarten and new clothes were in order—a couple of pairs of new jeans, some shirts and sweaters.

'I'll take you,' said Beth. 'We can go to Richmond and buy what you need, and we'll have a hamburger and fries for lunch. Maybe there's a movie you'd like to see. We can do that in the afternoon.'

His little body tensed all over. 'No,' he said tightly. 'I don't wanna go with you. You know nothing about it. I wanna go with Dad. He always goes with me.'

His eyes were angry, hostile and a wave of despair washed over her. He'd been halfway congenial in the past week. It seemed he had accepted her presence in the house, tolerated it at least. Why did she feel hurt about his rejection?

'I thought you might like to go with me this time.'

'No.' He didn't even raise his voice. He sounded hard and determined, too old for his age.

'All right, then, you don't have to.'

'Good.' He turned and walked off, and Beth gazed after him, suppressing a sudden, overwhelming urge to cry.

Reid took him shopping the next morning and they

were back before one. By the set of his mouth Beth could tell that Reid had seen happier times. Josh was wildly angry.

'I don't wanna sandwich!' he yelled. 'I wanna hamburger and fries! I wanna see a movie!'

'You sit down and eat your sandwich. I didn't promise you a hamburger, and I didn't promise you a movie.'

'But *she* did!' He pointed an accusing finger at Beth.

'Her name is Beth.' Reid's voice was suddenly icy calm. 'And you refused her offer to go shopping with you. You had your choice, young man, you live with the consequences.'

'I'm not eating this rotten, stupid peanut butter sandwich!'

Beth was shaking—not because of what Josh was saying, but because she felt at fault. They were having this fight because of her. She was coming between them, a realisation that shocked her to the core. Clumsily she came to her feet, only wanting to get away now, but Reid stopped her.

'Sit down, Beth.' His voice was very quiet, his eyes calm. He turned to Josh. 'Go to your room and wait there.' There was steel in his voice, now, and Josh walked out of the room without another word. There was no doubt that he recognised the limits to which he could go, and he had reached them now.

Beth's appetite had disappeared. Pushing away her half-eaten sandwich, she got up. 'I'll make some coffee.'

'Please.'

Silence reigned until she handed him his cup. He took it from her and met her gaze.

'Don't look so stricken, Beth.'

'You don't know how I feel,' she said miserably.

'I think I do. But I want you to understand that this has nothing to do with you personally.'

'But I'm the catalyst, right?'

Reid nodded slowly. 'I think so.'

'It doesn't make me feel any better, Reid. I . . . I keep thinking . . .'

'No.' He shook his head. 'No, Beth, please . . .' He took her hand and looked deep into her eyes. 'Promise me.'

Her throat went dry. 'Promise you what?'

CHAPTER FOUR

SHE didn't know why she was asking. The answer was in his eyes. He had known what she had been about to say—that she wanted to leave because she didn't want to make Josh so unhappy, to come between father and son.

'Promise me you won't leave yet,' Reid said quietly. 'You have another month. Please stay with us.'

She looked at him, not knowing what to say, not knowing what was best for Josh, for him, for herself. Then she nodded in answer because somehow it was the only thing to do, and she couldn't explain it. And still she felt afraid for all three of them. There was no way of knowing where all this was going to lead to.

'Thank you.' Then he smiled. 'Just keep that boss of yours under control until you get back to work.'

She grimaced. 'I keep wondering when he's going to call again. He will, you know.'

'Tell him to go to hell.'

'He'll just say he's been there already and it's not hot enough for him.'

Reid grinned. 'A tough one, right? Well, I wish you luck. I have great confidence in you.' He pushed his chair back. 'I think I'll have a talk with my son.'

'I'll go for a drive. I'll be back before dinner,' said Beth.

'Sure.' He smiled at her, eyes searching. 'Don't brood too much.'

Driving through the rolling countryside had a calming effect on her—green fields, hills covered with dark woods, cows grazing peacefully here and there, acres of corn, almost ripe.

I wish you luck. Reid's comment stuck in her mind for some reason. *I wish you luck.* Paul would never have said that. He'd have said, 'I'll take care of him for you,' or 'Leave him to me.'

Paul had wanted to take care of her and every detail in her life. He knew she was having trouble at work, and his solution had been marriage and kids and a house in suburbia. He had never understood her fierce resistance. It's no solution, she'd said so many times. It's a cop-out, don't you see?

No, he did not see. She had been exasperated with him and his old-fashioned view of the world. And still, in some incomplete, lopsided fashion, she had loved him. He was a warm and loving man and they'd had many happy times in the year they'd been together.

I wish you luck. Reid showed no inclination to play the Big Protector; she had to give him credit for that.

There wasn't much traffic on these country roads, and she went slowly, looking around, absorbing the peace of the quiet, sunny afternoon. Hay bales lay waiting in the fields, huge and round, rolled up like giant jelly rolls.

Such a change from city life. Beth pictured the huge square blocks of city buildings, her office, equally square, windowless and air-conditioned. In there, she had no idea what the weather was like outside.

She stopped the car at an intersection in front of a country store. The paint was peeling from the building. Empty boxes lay piled up in front of a grimy window. Some crates of empty bottles were stacked up in front. On the other side of the door, brightly coloured soft-drink machines cheered up the exterior.

As she opened the door, a bell rang and an old

woman came from the back of the store and greeted her. Beth looked around, not sure what it was she wanted. She was hungry now and needed something to eat.

'I didn't have any lunch,' she said to the lady, and smiled. The woman launched into a reply, more of a monologue, that Beth had trouble understanding. The local variety of English was a challenge, especially when spoken by the older generation who had never spoken anything else. Beth answered as best she could, half guessing at the woman's words. She felt like a foreigner. Where was she from? the woman wanted to know, and when she answered Washington, the woman nodded knowingly. Nobody speaking like Beth could come from Southern Virginia. She spoke of Washington as if it were a thousand miles away.

Beth bought crackers and a packet of sliced cheese and a container of drinking yogurt. Her eyes caught the splash of crimson of a huge sucker, and on impulse she bought that too. Maybe Josh would like it and laugh at the funny face decorated on the lollipop.

Was she trying to buy his love? Baking chocolate chip cookies, promising hamburgers and movies, bringing him this crazy gigantic sucker that was disastrous for his teeth? The thought bothered her.

She came home at five and made herself a cup of coffee. Reid was outside stacking firewood and Josh was trying to help. She went out to say hello and sat down on a big tree stump to watch them.

'Let me finish my coffee and I'll give you a hand,' she said, and Reid laughed.

'You're allowed to be lazy. Just think what it'll do to your fingernails.'

She grimaced. 'Not much. Look.' Her nails were clipped and filed short. She'd felt ridiculous with her neat long polished nails trying to milk a goat or fish for bass.

He glanced at her hands. 'My God!' he exclaimed in feigned horror. 'A real peasant, you are!'

All through dinner Josh was amazingly subdued. When Reid got up to answer the phone he looked at Beth nervously and tried to say something, but no words came.

'What's the matter, Josh?'

'I'm supposed . . . supposed to say I'm sorry.'

'For what, Josh?'

'For . . . for hurting your feelings. You wanted to go shopping with me and I didn't want to go with you.'

'Well, it's all right. We can do something else together another time.'

He nodded wordlessly, looking at his plate.

'Josh?' She waited until he looked up. 'Josh, I'd like to be your friend.'

He was silent, his expression full of helpless misery.

'It's all very difficult, isn't it? You feel very angry sometimes, don't you?'

He nodded. 'Yes.' It was barely a whisper.

His confusion wrenched at her heart. She wanted so much to put her arms around him, but it wasn't time for that yet.

Reid sat down again and looked from Beth to Josh and back. She nodded and smiled, and he grinned in answer.

He looked down on Josh and ruffled his hair. 'So, old man, how's your dinner?'

'It's okay. I don't like the beans, though.'

'All right, leave the beans for tonight.'

'Really?' Josh was delighted. He dug into the rest of his food and finished it in record time. He jumped out of his chair. 'Can I watch TV?'

Reid rolled his eyes and groaned in despair.

Reid was outside a few days later when the phone rang. Beth answered, immediately sorry when she realised it was Jack.

'How are you?' he asked.

'Do you care?' she asked bitterly.

'Of course I do, sweetheart. The better you are, the better I am.'

'Can't you handle the job without me, Jack?'

'Of course I can. But I miss you. I miss your smile and your beautiful, voluptuous . . .'

'Shut up, Jack! Come to the point!'

'We have a new account and I want you for it. It's the perfect job for you.' He began to explain, his voice cool and businesslike, as if he'd turned a switch.

She listened. She had to listen.

'Jack,' she said when he'd finished, 'you can find someone else to do the job. I'm not coming back until three weeks from now.'

'I can't wait three weeks, dammit!'

'You'll have to! Find someone else for this one. I don't particularly care, anyway.'

'What do you mean, you don't care? It's a big campaign!'

Beth gave a deep sigh. 'To tell you the truth, Jack, bubble gum doesn't turn me on. There's enough bubble gum in the world already.'

'What does that have to do with anything, for God's sake! It's not for you to decide, now is it? We're in the business of advertising, remember? Don't start this rubbish on me!' He was mad, and so was Beth.

'If you don't like it, fire me! But leave me alone!' She slammed the phone down and walked to a chair with shaking knees. Holding her hands stretched out in front of her, she noticed they were trembling.

'*Fire me!*' she'd said, and she hadn't really cared at the moment. She wasn't sure that she cared now. But it was dangerous. A moment of insanity could change one's life. She couldn't afford to risk anything in a moment of madness.

The front door opened and closed and a moment later Reid entered the kitchen.

'So,' he said, giving her a quick looking over, 'the bastard called again, I can tell.'

'Oh, you shut up too!' she snapped in frustration.

'All right,' he said in amiable tones, 'I'll shut up.' He picked up the paper and sat down across from her and started reading, blocking himself from view. Beth looked at the back of the paper and felt like screaming. It was silent for a long time, and without wanting to, her eyes glanced over the print. Something about the import of art, a piece about war souvenirs in Zimbabwe. There was an ad for men's wear. The models were young and handsome. One had a beard, a checked sports shirt and bedroom eyes; the other wore a windbreaker and had a leering smile. Come with me, baby, his face said, and I'll show you what true ecstasy is.

Beth sighed and the paper came down.

'That was a very deep sigh,' commented Reid. 'Something wrong?'

'No. Just my half-hourly sigh.'

His eyebrows rose in surprise. 'Your *what*?'

'My half-hourly sigh. People sigh about every thirty minutes or so, didn't you know? The lungs need to expand every now and then. Physiological necessity.'

He looked at his watch. 'Your last sigh was four minutes ago. And the one before that was seven minutes ago.'

'Nobody's perfect.'

He gave her a slow grin. 'But you come close.'

The tone of his voice made her grow warm. 'You're nice. Now if only I could believe it myself, I'd be in a lot better shape.'

'Why don't you feel good about yourself? Are you still blaming yourself for what happened at that presentation?'

'Yes.' She looked away. 'Jack wants me to come back, and I'm scared stiff.'

'Why? Because you think it might happen again?'

She nodded. 'I know it will happen again. And it makes me so mad. I feel like such a . . . weakling.' She raised her hands in a gesture of helplessness. 'I don't even know how to explain. All I know is . . . that I can't stand the pressure, people looking over my shoulder, phones ringing, people in and out of my office all day long. A wants this and B wants that. Deadlines. Changes here and changes there. A re-do of this and a re-do of that, and you'd better not step on anybody's tender little toes or bruise their precious little egos. Oh, God, I go crazy just thinking about it!' She covered her face with her hands.

'Then why are you in this line of work? Who says you have to do this?'

'It's not the work itself,' she said tonelessly. 'I can do that. It's everything around it. And I'm in this line of work because that's where I started off. It was fun at first. I was good, I got promoted. That's the way it goes in this world! Don't ask for the obvious!'

'I'm asking,' Reid said calmly, 'who says you have to do this?' He looked straight at her. 'Just saying that's the way it goes isn't good enough. You can't let your life be prescribed by general rules and expectations. You have responsibility for your own health and sanity.

You're here now, away from it all. Try to take a good look at yourself, your life, what it is you really want. All this drive and ambition and competition isn't right for everybody.'

'I had ambition and competition for breakfast, lunch and dinner during my entire childhood! I was brought up on it! I don't know anything else!'

'Not necessarily a nutritious diet,' he said dryly.

Beth shoved her chair back and stood up. 'Oh, you know it all, don't you! Sitting here in this godforsaken hole playing the peasant with your goat and your chickens and your pretty little garden . . . and . . . and . . .' Tears overwhelmed her and one sob followed another, and she couldn't speak any more. She was holding on to a chair and he was with her seconds later, pulling her into his arms.

'I'm not the enemy, Beth,' he said softly. 'I'm on *your* side, don't you understand?'

'Then . . . then leave me alone!' She struggled and he withdrew slightly, taking her hands in a firm clasp.

'How can I? Look at yourself—you're shaking, you're crying. Beth, I want you to understand that no one, *nobody* is sending you back to your job. You don't *have* to go. *You're* the *only one* who makes that decision for you. And Beth . . .' he lifted her face, '. . . you're not a loser because you decide something isn't right for you. It may take a lot more courage to do that than to fight a losing battle.'

She closed her eyes and leaned against him. Inside her a struggle was going on. She heard the words he was speaking, but didn't want to understand, wanted to push out the truth of their meaning. Quitting was for losers—another concept she'd grown up with. You didn't quit, you fought on to the bitter end, because only then could you win.

'Quitting is for losers,' she whispered.

'Not all battles are worth fighting, Beth.'

'You don't understand! I can't give up a career just like that. I've worked so hard! It's my life, my livelihood. It's the way I make a living. It's what gives me self-respect and self-esteem. I . . .' She paused for only a moment. 'Reid, I'm good at what I do. I have talent for this sort of work. How can I give it up? I'll have nothing left.'

'You'll have your talent left, your creativity. You'll always have that. Nobody can take that away from you. There are other ways to use what you have. Other jobs, for instance.'

She swung away from him, pulling her hands out of his grasp. 'Oh, it's so easy, isn't it?' she said bitterly. 'Another job! What? Where? How?'

'It's not easy, Beth,' he said quietly. 'I know, I did it myself.'

She stared at him. 'You wanted to. You needed to, because of Josh,' she said slowly.

'I didn't *have* to, Beth. I *decided* to, because Josh became my number one priority.'

There was nothing she could say to that.

'Beth, you have to decide what your priorities are— your health and happiness, or the world's esteem of your work. There's a lot of extra pressure on women these days. They have to work harder to prove themselves, but if you can't do what you're doing it's not because you happen to be a woman. It's because you don't have the personality for it, because you as a person are not right for the job. There's nothing wrong in that. And it has nothing to do with weakness.'

She felt miserable and confused and torn apart. 'I don't know any more, I just don't know.'

'Come here.' He took her in his arms again, holding

her tight against him. 'It feels very good doing this,' he said softly. 'I'd just like to hold you like this and tell you all kinds of nice and wonderful things, but I think I'd better not.'

'Why not?' she whispered, heart hammering. 'My ego needs it.'

He withdrew slightly and smiled down at her. 'You're a very special lady, nice to have around.'

'*Lady!* Makes me feel like a grandma!'

'Girl?'

Beth shook her head. 'I'm way past that.'

'Woman?'

'That's it.' She looked into his eyes. They were full of smiling lights, and her stomach tightened nervously.

'Don't look at me like that—you make me nervous.'

Reid grinned. 'Please don't hurt me.'

'What . . .'

He kissed her, and words and thoughts got lost. His hands reached up and held her head. She felt his fingers move through her hair, and it felt oddly intimate and sensual. Moving closer to him, she responded instinctively, and then sudden fear sprang up inside her. 'Reid,' she whispered against his mouth, 'Reid . . . I want us to stop.' She wanted to cry. She loved him. All these weeks it had been building up. She'd been with him much of the time, watching him work, watching him with Josh. And loving him was making everything so complicated.

His eyes were dark and the expression in them shook her. A shiver went through her. 'I'm sorry.'

His jaw tightened and a muscle moved in his cheek. He turned around without another word and walked out the door into the night.

*

On the outside nothing much changed, but tension reigned for the next week. Beth didn't understand what it was that had happened to him, to her. The whole atmosphere had changed, nothing tangible, nothing she could put her finger on, but it was there, as real as the darkness at night. Reid was in Richmond several days. Other times he was home, cutting trees in the woods behind the pond, repairing a leaky roof in the chicken house, fishing in the evening and early morning.

Her moods ranged between anger and pain. Was it her fault? What had she done, in the first place? Was he mad at her for saying no? Well, if that was all it took he had a very tiny little ego, and she didn't care. If his ego depended on his conquests in bed, she wanted no part of him. Well, somehow she didn't think his ego was the problem. If he'd been after her body he'd have started the day she arrived.

She'd been crazy to come. She stood at the counter peeling potatoes for dinner. It was her own stupid fault. What had she expected, isolating herself with a man like him out in the sticks? Nature had a way of doing what it was supposed to be doing. Here she was, angry with herself because of her failure to be what she wanted to be, falling to pieces all over the place, and Reid, conveniently there to rescue the maiden in distress . . . A look, a touch, a kiss, and Mother Nature was smiling smugly down from the clouds.

Well, she could stop smiling. Things weren't working out the way she had intended. Romeo was licking his wounds in the woods, and Juliet was weeping while peeling potatoes.

She wiped the back of her hand across her eyes. Damn him! Mr Know-It-All had the answers to everything, only she didn't agree with them. In two weeks' time she would get in her car and drive back to

Washington and start living a normal life again. Not this phoney fairy-tale existence in a house with grass on its roof. She would go back to her apartment—a plain old ordinary apartment on the sixth floor of a twelve-storey building sitting very much on top of the ground. She'd go to work in the morning, say Hi to Jack and every other maniac in the office, and make a full pot of coffee and get down to work. She'd do the very best possible job, a *brilliant* job on that bubble gum account, if it was still there, or otherwise whatever else came up—zippers, dish sponges, deodorant. What did it matter?

She threw the potato peeler in the sink and washed the potatoes. She looked at the clock. Might as well start frying the chicken. Why was she doing this? This wasn't in the agreement when she'd come here. Keep an eye on Josh when his father was gone—that was all, period. And here she was, cooking dinner, doing laundry, milking a stupid goat. To hell with it!

Leaving everything the way it was, she got her handbag from her room, combed her hair and got in her car. Josh was with his father and nobody needed her.

She drove around aimlessly for more than an hour, then turned on to Route 64 and headed for Richmond. A treat was what she needed—a nice dinner in a fancy restaurant. She looked down at her clothes. But not dressed like this in jeans and a shirt. She could go to a store and buy new clothes. A dress, shoes, pantyhose—why not?

She drove around downtown Richmond looking around for a store. Seeing the sign of a rather classy department store, she parked the car and went in.

Forty-five minutes later she marched out with everything she needed in a bag. She turned around and dashed right back in. In the ladies' room she changed into her new things, cutting price tags and tickets with a nail clipper. Having stuffed her jeans, shirt and sandals into the bag, she casually strolled out of the store, wondering if she might look suspicious and be picked up for shoplifting. Her sales receipts were safely in her wallet, so she should be covered, still it felt strange to walk out the store wearing brand new things acquired only minutes earlier.

It was almost nine and she was hungry. It was quite a restaurant she walked into, even fancier than she had imagined, with suited waiters and an atmosphere of quiet chic. Good, she thought. Live it up, baby.

The face of the maître d'hotel was totally inscrutable when he asked if she had a reservation. No, she said, looking right at him, no reservation. Was she waiting for someone to join her? No, she was alone.

She could see the flicker in his eyes, and raised herself up to her full five-eight and stared him right in the face. 'I would like a good table, please,' she said in a firm tone, knowing full well that he might just try sticking her in a corner near the kitchen. No, sir, don't let him try that on her! She was a lady alone, dining out alone, expecting impeccable service. A moment of hesitation in the pale eyes, then a slight nod and an invitation to follow him.

It was not the best table available, but neither was it the worst, so she had no reason to complain.

Ordering an extravagant meal of lobster thermidor and the usual trimmings was probably ridiculous, but she did it anyway. It took too long for it to arrive, and as she waited Beth felt quite at a loss, having no one to talk to, and nothing to do but look around or examine her fingernails. She sipped the water, having declined to order a cocktail. She was aware that two men, business people by the looks of them, were scrutinising her covertly. Respectable women didn't dine out alone, not in a place as sophisticated as this. They might grab a quick bite in some hamburger joint, but they didn't dress up and sit alone through an elaborate dinner. Unless they had ulterior motives.

Beth let her eyes slide slowly over them, showing no interest, but noticing they were talking now and laughing at something. Maybe they were planning to pick her up.

She choked at the water as an unrestrained giggle escaped her and got smothered in the water. She spluttered and coughed, and sure enough, from the corner of her eye she noticed one of the men approaching her table. She groaned inwardly and straightened in her chair.

'Are you all right, ma'am?'

'Thank you, yes.'

He was tall, fortyish, with thinning hair and small eyes that darted up and down quickly, taking in every detail of her appearance.

'I see you're alone. Would you care to join us?' He motioned vaguely to his table where his partner was feigning uninterest.

She didn't like those two. They were on the prowl, no doubt about that.

She looked at him coolly. 'It's very kind of you to offer, but no, thank you.' There was no warmth in her voice. She glanced at his left hand and saw a wide solid gold band. The jerk hadn't even had the foresight to take off his ring! Her eyes lingered on his hand intentionally, then slowly moved up to his face. She smiled. 'Maybe you should call your wife.'

There was a look of such perplexity on the man's face that Beth could barely restrain her laughter. For a moment he stood still as a statue, then turned on his heel and marched off.

Her food arrived and the waiter eyed her suspiciously as he noticed the man retreating to his own table. They didn't like this kind of thing in nice, respectable restaurants, Beth knew very well. Single men were all right, but unaccompanied ladies were at least suspect.

She wanted very much to enjoy the food, but didn't. A nagging uneasiness had now replaced her earlier anger and discontent. Sitting down, she'd finally started collecting her thoughts and suddenly all she wanted to do was go home.

Why had she done such a silly thing? she asked herself as she drove back through the dark countryside. She'd spent an outrageous amount of money for clothes and shoes she didn't really need—she had enough clothes at home. And eating a gourmet dinner alone while mentally and visually being pawed over by two lecherous womanisers was hardly good for the digestion.

She'd wanted to get away—from the tension between Reid and herself, from the fear inside her. She had intended, *fully* intended to stay in the country for a while to recuperate, to get herself together and go back to work. Now she was more confused than when she'd arrived. She didn't know if she should go back any more. Reid's words kept hanging on in her consciousness, confusing the issue. And there was something else. Their relationship had become a nerve-racking situation, all underground and unrevealed, but very much there. She wished desperately that she knew what he really felt about her.

She parked the car and went into the house. A small lamp burned in the living room. There was a light on in Reid's workroom, and the door was ajar. It swung all the way open as soon as she set foot in the house. Reid stood in the doorway, arms up and braced against the doorposts.

She stood still and watched him. His face was hard to read with the bright light coming from behind him.

'I didn't know you had plans for tonight,' he said, his voice toneless.

'I didn't know either. It sort of came up.' Why was she standing there without moving? Was she waiting? For what? Her stomach clenched uneasily.

'I would have appreciated a note. You know, a piece of paper with a couple of words on it.' There was a calm, cold anger in his tone. 'And don't tell me it's none of my business what you do with your free time. I don't care where you went or what you did. I'm talking about common courtesy. I don't like people disappearing into the night without an inkling of why!' His hands came down and he jammed them into his pockets, and advanced into the room.

Beth stared at him, saying nothing.

He stood in front of her, eyeing her dress. 'Where the hell did you go dressed up like that?'

'It's irrelevant to the discussion,' she said icily. 'I offer you my apologies for not telling you I was leaving.'

Silence surrounded them, and his eyes examined her face. 'You were in the middle of getting dinner, and you must have walked out, just like that,' he said slowly. 'I waited for an hour. I called Daisy, but you weren't there. I called the corner general store and they hadn't seen you. So I fixed dinner for Josh and me. I put him to bed, but he couldn't go to sleep. Nine o'clock and he was still awake.' His eyes pierced into hers. 'He wanted to know where you were and when you would be back, and I had to tell him I didn't know. He wanted to look in your room and make sure your stuff wasn't all gone.'

The pause was interminable. 'You should have seen the relief on his face when he saw your clothes hanging in the closet. I don't relish invading other people's privacy, but I couldn't help it. I had to do something.'

There was a sick feeling in her stomach. 'I'm sorry,' she said, slowly sitting down in a chair.

'You think he dislikes you, don't you?' His voice was very low now.

Beth nodded.

'I wouldn't be so sure about that.' He turned and strode back into his office, closing the door with finality.

A whole night on the town and she felt worse now than when she'd left. Why had she gone anyway? A gesture, revolt in disguise. Revolt against what? Wearily she got up and went into her bedroom and began to take off her clothes. She hung the dress on a hanger in the closet, and put her new shoes underneath it. She'd always enjoyed having nice clothes, enjoyed buying something new. This was a beautiful, sophisticated dress, but she found no joy in it now. All she saw before her was Josh's face. He hadn't been able to sleep because she was not home.

Her robe hung over a chair, and she put it on and left the room. Opening Josh's door silently, she tiptoed towards the bed. Curled up in a bundle, he lay beneath the thin cover, one little fist pressed against his cheek. She looked at him in the dim light, at the soft smooth little face, the dark curls straying over his forehead, and a wave of warmth and tenderness washed over her. He was so small, so vulnerable. And so frightened.

Crouching down, she put her hand lightly on his

head. 'Josh,' she whispered, 'I'm back.' She didn't want to wake him, just hoped her words would somehow penetrate his sleep.

He made a small sound and then he smiled. His eyes didn't open and he didn't wake, but she knew he had heard.

She stood up slowly and turned towards the door, and Reid was standing there, watching her.

CHAPTER FIVE

HE stepped aside to let her pass. How long had he been standing there? She turned and faced him. 'Josh's all right, all covered up,' she said evenly.

'Thank you.'

He didn't move, looking ahead of him as if thinking of something. Tension was thick as fog. It had been all week. She'd been breathing it and tasting it every hour of the day.

'What are you going to tell him when I leave in a couple of weeks?'

'The truth. He knows you have to go, but he wasn't expecting you to leave just yet.'

'I'm sorry I've upset him.'

He didn't reply, and she turned to go.

'I'm going to bed. Goodnight.'

'Wait a minute.' Reid sounded angry. 'What the hell is going on? Why are you being so damn hostile?'

'I'm not hostile. I'm tired, that's all.'

And I'm in love with you, she wanted to add, and it makes me miserable. You drive me crazy. I have problems enough right now.

But what she wanted to do right now was forget about all that, to put her head on his shoulder and her arms around his neck. Kiss me, she wanted to say, hold me, make love to me. She wanted to cry.

Reid was staring at her with a strange look on his face. 'I don't like what's been happening this last week,' he said slowly. 'The atmosphere has been rather bumpy, to put it mildly.'

94

'You've been treating me like a stranger.' She swallowed hard. 'You've been keeping your distance, haven't you? What's the matter? Are you scared or something?'

He looked straight at her. 'Are you?' he asked slowly.

'Me? Am I scared? No, why?' There was anger in her voice now, and rebellion.

'You *know*, Beth, don't ask.'

She whirled around. 'I'm going to my room.'

He took her arm in one quick movement. 'I think we'd better talk about it, don't you?'

Anger rushed up. 'No, I don't think so. Let go of my arm!'

'Do you always run away from unpleasantness? Run around in circles without making decisions? Hoping somehow that if you wait long enough the problem will go away? Let me . . .'

Shaking with anger, she glared at him. 'Who gave you the right to analyse me? How dare you criticise me? Judge me? Who the hell do you think you are?'

'I know who I am,' he said calmly. 'Do you know who you are?'

'The Queen of England! Now let me go!' He twisted her arm so she turned towards him both his arms came around her, trapping her.

'Don't!' She struggled to regain her freedom, but it was no use. I should have taken judo lessons, she thought bitterly. One simple movement and he would have been sprawled at my feet now. Oh, she would have enjoyed doing that!

Jaws clenched, she glared at him in icy anger. 'You just have to use your physical strength, don't you? It's the one thing I find totally despicable in a man!'

'Sometimes we have to stoop low,' he agreed calmly.

'I don't want to fight, most certainly not physically, but I do want to talk. And I do want you to stay here and listen.'

'I don't want to talk! I don't want your opinions or your analysis or your advice! I wonder why I ever agreed to come here!'

'So do I.'

Everything else she wanted to say got stuck in her throat at his quiet reply. There was an intense light in his eyes that made her shiver. She said nothing.

'I think we need a little clearing of the air after all these weeks. I don't see any reason for us to play peek-a-boo with each other. The messages are coming through loud and clear!'

Beth stood in his arms, rigid, not answering. There was no way she was going to discuss this. There was no way she was going to have an affair with him. Period.

Oh, God, she thought, what am I thinking? Who am I fooling? Why can't I make up my mind about anything? No wonder I'm such a wreck. I can't decide about my work, my life, my love life. One moment I want this, the next I want that.

'Say something!' Reid stepped back without releasing her and looked at her with anger radiating from him.

'All right.' Suddenly she felt icy calm. 'All right, I'll say something. I came here for more reasons than one, which I'm sure doesn't surprise you. Talking to you at Doc's party, I fell for you hook, line and sinker. I'm also quite aware that you invited me here for more reasons than one. So here we are. In two weeks I'm going back to D.C. We can manage two weeks, can't we?'

'I wish you'd drop the nasty tone,' he said, releasing

her and leaning back against the wall. 'And I wish you'd tell me why you feel so bad about all this. We're both reacting in a very normal way. What's the matter, Beth? Do you mistrust me?'

'Yes—no.' She hugged herself, arms crossed in front of her chest. 'I don't know.'

A sudden smile warmed his face. 'Well now, that's what I call a clear answer—yes, no, I don't know.'

'I suppose I don't trust myself a whole lot either,' she said. 'I haven't been very lucky in love, so far.'

'Neither have I.'

A terrible sadness swept over her. She thought of Josh's mother, of her own empty life, of Paul's face when she'd told him she didn't want to get married. She thought of her overwhelming feeling for the man standing in front of her. She thought of her small apartment, coming home alone, going to bed alone. She could do it for ever if she had to, only she didn't want to.

'I'm scared.' She was surprised to hear herself say the words. 'I think first of all I have to straighten out my career problems before I dive head first into another disaster.'

He laughed then. 'You're a positive thinker! I wasn't planning on the two of us going into disaster together.'

Beth was silent for a moment. 'I'll go home tomorrow if you prefer.'

'Do you want to?'

She looked at him and shook her head slowly. 'No.'

'Then stay.' He stepped towards her and gave her a quick kiss on her hair. 'Go to bed.' He turned and strode into his study, saying goodnight before he closed the door.

Nothing had been resolved. Nothing.

*

A strange persistent screeching woke her in the middle of the night. It was a small, shrill sound coming from somewhere in the room. A cricket.

The sound went on endlessly, vibrating in the air, seeming to grow louder and shriller as the minutes passed. Beth cursed the little monster, which didn't help: She threatened him with some evil spell, which left him unimpressed. She covered her head with the thin blanket, but the sound was still there. The only thing to do—if she wanted to sleep—was to catch the beast and get rid of it.

For a few moments she listened carefully. It seemed to come from the left side of the room. Turning on the bedside light, she swung her legs over the side of the bed and sat up. The closet? Softly she moved over to the wardrobe and carefully opened the double doors, and immediately the nerve-racking chirping intensified. She couldn't see a thing because she was blocking the light, and she groaned in disgust. How was she going to find it? How she was going to *catch* it was another question. Going down on her knees, she tried to see. The sound was coming from the right-hand corner where she'd put her sandals and sneakers.

With an exasperated sigh she began to move her suitcase out of the way, putting it behind her in the room where it fell over on the carpet with a dull thud. She shoved the hangers with her clothes to the left so she'd have some room to move.

A closet was not the place to catch a cricket in the dead of night. God, the noise he made! He sounded like a ten-pound something. Where was he hiding? Or was it a she? No, it was the male of the species that made all the noise. Was he in the corner? Inside one of her sneakers? Maybe he'd had the audacity to crawl into one of her brand-new pumps. Carefully she took her sandals and tossed them out. He wasn't to be seen any place, but the shrill noise was vibrating all around her. Gently she picked up one of her sneakers and from somewhere the little terror leaped over her hand into a corner.

She reached for him blindly, lost her balance and crashed into the closet door. She swore under her breath and rubbed her shoulder. She'd probably woken somebody up with her racket.

Right she was. Reid pushed his way through the door a mere second later, sleepy-eyed and naked.

'What the hell . . .' He stopped, looking down at her on the floor with unconcealed amazement. His eyes skimmed the suitcase on the floor, the sandals, the sneakers. 'Are you packing? Are you out of your mind?'

'No and yes! I'm *not* packing and I *am* just about to go out of my mind. There's a *cricket* in my closet and it makes more noise than the Washington Philharmonic!' She looked at him furiously, as if it were his fault, as if he'd put the stupid insect in her closet. 'And go and put something on!'

His face collapsed and he began to laugh, a sound coming from deep inside him. 'You should see yourself . . . this would make a great picture. Don't move, I'll get my camera.'

'And I'll get mine!'

Reid hadn't moved from the spot, his face one big grin as he watched her. 'All right, no pictures.' His eyes swept around the room and in one swift movement he fished her robe off the chair and somehow wrapped it around his waist. 'This better?'

'Charming.'

Deliberately slowly he let his gaze travel over her body. Wearing only a flimsy, low-cut teddy that left shoulders, arms as well as the full length of her legs exposed and the rest of her faintly visible through the thin, shimmery lavender material, she might as well have been naked.

'What happened to nightgowns?' he asked.

'They got some competition. And stop staring at me!' And then it was as if she did see herself, and him, and the picture they would make together, and she began to laugh, slowly, then harder and he joined in. She had never felt so silly in her life.

She sat down on her knees again and peered into the closet. 'Why don't you catch this little tyrant for me?'

Reid knelt beside her, silky robe and all. 'I'll try.'

The cricket was quiet now. Not a sound from the closet. Their heads close together, they listened. Beth was barely breathing. Nothing, not the tiniest little chirp. Reid turned his face sideways and looked at her. 'Are you sure there's one in here?' he whispered. 'Maybe you just dreamed it.'

'No, I didn't!' she whispered fiercely.

'Maybe you scared him to death.'

'Maybe.' Did crickets have heart attacks?

Silence reigned.

Their faces were almost touching. She could feel the warmth of him radiating on to her skin. Her heart was racing as if she were running a marathon. The tension was becoming unbearable.

Do something, you stupid cricket, she prayed. Chirp, screech, cackle, bark, *anything*. Save me.

'Beth?' His voice was barely audible.

'What?' She looked at him, blood pounding in her ears.

'I don't hear a cricket.'

'Neither do I.'

They looked at each other, slowly moving even

closer together, and it wasn't by conscious movement, it just happened. He put both his hands on top of her head and smoothed her hair in soft, gentle strokes, over and over again. Then slowly his hands began to move down her neck and shoulders, then softly down her arms until he held each hand in one of his. They looked small and white in his large brown ones and Beth gazed at them in wonder. Were those really her hands?

He curved his fingers around hers, caressing them one by one, touching each finger as if it were some delicate treasure.

This gentle, seemingly innocent touching of her hands stirred her more than many other, more intimate caresses had ever done before. No man had ever paid so much attention to her hands. It was a miracle she should feel this way, a miracle that touching of their hands could evoke such feelings.

He took her hands and lifted them, putting them down on his shoulders and his hands slid up her arms, coming to rest at the nape of her neck.

His eyes were bright and intense as they gazed into hers.

Please, she pleaded silently, don't do this. But it was only one small part of her talking, and the whole big rest of her was crying out for more.

Curling her fingers into his hair, she felt the wiry texture of it, soft and rough at the same time—like Reid himself, she thought in surprise. A rough man with a soft heart.

'What are you thinking?' he whispered, sliding his hands down her back.

'That I like your hair. It feels good. First time I saw you I wanted to touch your hair and feel it.'

He smiled at that, sitting up on his knees and pulling her very close, his face against hers, his mouth on her cheek. 'You go ahead and touch it all you want. You know what I noticed about you that night we met? Your voice. You have a very sexy voice. I was prepared to sit there all night and listen to you talk.'

Her robe had fallen away from around his waist. She took a steadying breath. 'You're naked,' she said as if accusing him of some terrible crime.

'I'm not,' he whispered.

'You are, too. Did you think that slithery thing was going to stay put?'

He grinned. 'No, did you?'

'Reid,' she said desperately, 'please get out of here.' Please don't, the other part of her said.

'Beth . . .' He began to kiss her again and she felt herself go weak with longing. She wished she had sense enough to push him away, to tell him to get out of her room with his gentle touches and soft words. She felt feverish and out of control and helpless. Damn the cricket!

You rotten monster of an insect, she thought. You got me into this, now get me out.

Reid moved down the straps of her teddy and it slid down to her hips. She couldn't move. She closed her eyes, feeling his hands on her body with the same gentle touching. A feverish warmth surged through her and it seemed suddenly hard to breathe.

She opened her eyes and put her hands on his. 'Don't,' she whispered. 'Please don't.'

He removed his hands, his face suddenly totally expressionless. With shaking fingers she pulled the straps back over her shoulders.

'Please . . .' Her voice shook. 'Please go.'

'Certainly.' He leaped to his feet, turning away from her, and made for the door.

Then a shrill screeching filled the room and Reid

stopped, doorknob in hand. He stood still for only a moment, his back turned to her, then he stepped out into the hall, closing the door behind him.

It washed over her then—a bitter anger and a hollow pain. She felt like lashing out at something or somebody. The cricket screeched louder and louder, filling her mind with its shrill sounds until she could take no more. Picking up a sneaker, she flung it into the corner of the closet from where the sounds were coming. She hurled another one after it, then a sandal, each with a violent, explosive force.

The cricket was silent. Breathing hard, Beth sat and waited. A moment later, the shrill sound was back, and with renewed, furious desperation she reached for another sandal, knowing in the back of her mind that her efforts were useless. Her eyes caught the door opening and through a haze of angry tears she saw Reid coming in. Her brain registered the blue blur of jeans. She hadn't known she had been crying.

He sat down next to her on the floor and with gentle fingers began to wipe away the tears on her face. She sat totally still, looking at his face as he was watching her. He said nothing, not a word, and she loved him for it. She loved him for his silence, and for the gentleness of his gestures and the kindness in his eyes.

The cricket sounded like a false whistle.

'I'm going to get the little devil if it takes me all night,' he said in a voice that was soft but venomous. Crouching in front of the closet, he peered inside. Beth got out of the way and sat down on the edge of the bed. Her eyes slid over his brown back, his neck and shoulders, the back of his head. She thought of him touching her hands, of his fingers on her face. She imagined him making love to her. She felt miserable.

With a muffled battle-cry, Reid lurched forward into

the closet, then gave a whoop of triumph. Coming to his feet, he turned and showed her one of her new shoes, one hand holding it, the other covering the opening. 'I've got the little monster. Now if you'll open the kitchen door for me we'll send him back to his cronies.'

Beth scrambled up, hastily put on her robe and rushed to the kitchen on her bare feet. Outside, Reid put the shoe upside down in the grass and gave it a good shake. 'There you go, buddy, and don't you come back!'

Beth watched him from the doorway, arms folded across her chest. The air was warm and balmy, sweet with summer scents and full of the sounds of night.

He handed her the shoe. 'Here you go, all taken care of.'

She took the shoe and absently rubbed it with her forefinger. 'Thank you.' For some reason she felt terribly uncomfortable. 'I can't believe he had the gall to crawl into one of my new shoes,' she said, looking down on the dull shine of leather. 'I just bought them last night. The dress, too,' she babbled on, more afraid of the silence than anything else at this moment.

'Fast work,' he commented without particular inflection. He was watching her, leaning against the rock wall of the house, hands in his pockets.

'Something got into me last night. I just left. I went to Richmond and decided to treat myself to a fancy dinner. I was wearing jeans, so . . .' She let the rest of the sentence trail away.

'So?'

'I hadn't worn a dress for a month,' she said defensively. Oh, shut up! she told herself. The last thing he wants to hear about is your clothing problem.

'Is that important?'

'No.' She felt utterly silly.

'Did you have a nice dinner?'

'I had lobster thermidor,' she continued desperately. 'And it wasn't very nice. There were two guys looking me over, and one of them tried to pick me up. I told him to give his wife a call.'

She'd thought he'd smile, but he didn't.

'You don't like men throwing themselves at you, do you?'

His response surprised her and she wasn't sure how to interpret his words.

'Not any old stranger, no.'

'What about me?'

'You're not a stranger.'

'Then what's wrong, Beth?'

'I don't know,' she said dully. 'I don't think anything is *wrong*. I just think things aren't right. There's too much on my mind right now. My career, especially. In two weeks I'm going back to Washington, and that's three hours away from here.'

'Beth ...' Reid took a step forward, and for a moment she thought he was going to touch her, take her in his arms. Then he checked the movement and stood still, looking at her. 'Beth ... what I feel for you is very strong and very real,' he said quietly, 'but I'm not going to tell you that I love you, because I don't know. I'm very uncomfortable with that word. I know that sounds like a cop-out, and maybe it is, but I'm not going to say something I don't feel right about.'

She wasn't sure what she felt. She didn't want to feel anything. She looked straight into his eyes. 'I'm not expecting you to lie, and I'm not expecting you to tell me you love me.' Her voice sounded calm. She felt cold, despite the warm night air, and she shivered. The dark surrounded them, but it did not shield them from the feelings and emotions vibrating between them, the currents going back and forth, pushing, pulling.

'Thanks for catching the cricket,' she said when he did not reply. Her voice sounded forced and unnatural now. 'I'm going inside. Goodnight, Reid.'

She almost ran back to her room, afraid he might keep her from going, force her to talk more. Closing the door firmly behind her, she let out a deep sigh. She crawled into bed and curled up into a ball under the covers. Taking deep breaths, she tried to calm herself. Soon she'd be back in Washington and after a while this man and his boy living in their underground house would fade away into some small memory, disembodied from emotions.

She didn't believe it for a moment.

Ten in the morning, and Beth was sitting in a lawn chair with a cup of coffee and a magazine. Birds were making a racket in the apple tree. Ahead was the pasture with the little white goat pulling at some tufts of grass without much enthusiasm. Beyond was the shiny glimmer of the pond against the backdrop of woods and hills. The blue sky stretched peacefully out over it all.

Reid and Josh were out cutting more firewood for the winter. Soon they'd be back with another load. There was a lot of wood stacked up already, like a small wall running along the driveway close to the house.

Beth wondered what it would be like to sit around the woodstove in the winter. It conjured up images of old-fashioned winters when people stayed at home and read books instead of watching television, of warm family Christmases, hot chocolate, burning candles. But it was a hot summer day and the images in her mind lacked reality.

She felt very lazy and quite content sitting in the shade, doing nothing. A white butterfly fluttered before her face, then disappeared. She turned the page of her magazine and found herself looking at one of her own ads, a lingerie layout she'd worked on two years before. It was still running.

At first there'd been a lot of pride whenever she saw some of her own work displayed in magazines or papers. She was *still* proud. Her work was good. But now there were so many other emotions mixed up with it. Turning the page, she began to read an article on prescription drugs, but it couldn't hold her attention.

At times her mind played tricks with her. She didn't want to think about work. Still, in unguarded moments she found herself toying with visual and verbal ideas for a bubble gum commercial. She'd started working with TV in the last year, adding another dimension to her expertise.

When she was a child, bubble gum had been a favourite candy, a toy, really. Who could blow the biggest bubbles? And what to do when it collapsed all over your face? She remembered standing with a friend in front of the bathroom mirror giggling and laughing helplessly at their faces covered with pink or purple gum.

She wished she had more information, something to let her know what exactly it was the company wanted. Not that it mattered. She wasn't going to do it; she'd said so to Jack. He hadn't called in a week. She hoped she'd finally got through to him.

She was looking forward to going back to work. Her head was full of ideas and plans, full of new determinations. She felt up to a new start. Her next campaign was going to be the very best ever. She was going to make it to the top.

New enthusiasm made her feel lighter. Washington was an exciting place to work. New York was better. She grinned to herself. Madison Avenue, here I come!

There was the rumble of the red pick-up labouring slowly up the driveway, then the screeching of brakes. Reid jumped out and Josh leaped to the ground after him.

Beth went into the kitchen to get them each something cold to drink—water with ice for Reid, and apple juice for Josh. She carried the glasses out on a tray.

'Thanks.' Reid gulped down the water with only a few large swallows. 'God, it's hot!' He mopped his forehead with the back of his hand, giving her a fleeting glance.

Her chest felt tight. It's wrong, she thought suddenly, it's not right the way we are together, so restrained and unnatural and selfconscious. We should be having fun together, and not measuring every single word or gesture. The more she saw of him, the worse she felt.

She watched him standing in the back of the truck throwing out the wood on to a pile, one piece at a time. He had taken his shirt off and the sun was beating down on his bare brown back. Over six feet of virility, muscles tensing and relaxing—a beautiful, healthy male body. She thought again of his fingers touching her face.

Turning abruptly, she walked back into the house.

'You're going back soon, aren't you?' Josh asked one morning. Beth was cooking apple sauce to be canned later, peeling and slicing more apples for apple pie. Putting the knife down, she looked down on the suntanned face with the dark eyes. 'I'm going home next

Saturday or Sunday. I'm going back to work on Monday.'

'Yeah.' It came out casually. With his left foot he was making designs on the floor, his eyes looking down with interest. 'Maybe you can come back some time— you know, for a weekend or something.' His eyes were following the motions of his foot with great concentration.

Beth stirred the apple sauce. 'Maybe,' she said carefully.

'Yesterday I caught a baby frog in the woods,' he said out of the blue, his face lifting to hers. 'It was tiny tiny tiny.' He grinned mischievously, all guardedness gone. 'He peed on my hand.'

Beth laughed. 'That's because he was scared.'

'Yeah, that's what Dad said.' He sighed. 'I let him go, you know.'

'I'm glad you did. Did your dad tell you about the cricket in my shoe one night?'

'No!' His eyes were wide with interest. 'Tell me!'

She relayed the events, heavily censored, and with some exaggerated dramatics that left him laughing breathlessly.

'Oh, wow, that was funny!' He collapsed on a chair and leaned on the table as if utterly exhausted.

Beth turned the heat off under the pan of apple sauce, finished assembling the pie and put it into the oven.

'How about a snack? I'm going to have a cup of coffee and some of Grandma Daisy's carrot cake. Would you like some?'

He nodded. 'Can I have some orange juice, too?'

'Sure.' Beth was grateful for times like these, when Josh let down his guard or simply forgot he had decided not to be friendly to her. She hoped he would forget altogether one day and be himself with her.

Reid was in Richmond for the day for meetings and appointments dealing with his beloved housing development. He had asked her on several occasions to join him in his study to talk about various aspects of the job, asking her for ideas and opinions about the layout of the houses, or what she thought prospective buyers would think about the pros and cons.

From the very first time he had talked about his work she had been fascinated.

Josh went to play outside after he had scoffed down his cake. Beth cleaned up the kitchen and turned on the dishwasher, grimacing at the noise. Why did all those modern appliances have to make so much noise? Vacuum cleaners, washers, dishwashers, typewriters ... wasn't there anything they could do about it?

The grocery list was on the refrigerator, held down by a magnet the shape and colour of a strawberry. Pencil in hand, Beth contemplated the list, trying to remember what else needed to be added. Salt, that was it. And flour and pancake syrup. Maybe she should go out now and get the shopping done. Josh would like to come, but she hoped he wouldn't beg for every other bag of cookies or candies.

Reid wouldn't like it. He'd said if he needed a housekeeper he'd hire one. Beth was not a paid servant. He was quite capable of buying groceries himself. The cleaning woman was now coming twice a week, but there was still enough to do. Beth was part of the household now and she saw no reason why she shouldn't do her share.

She added a few more items to the list and as she lowered her hand to put the pencil down a sudden, agonising scream penetrated her consciousness.

'Beth! Beth!' The kitchen door was flung open and

Josh hurled himself inside, eyes wide with terror.

For one frozen moment she stared at him standing near the door, crying, sobbing. No blood anywhere. Her mind registered it immediately. She rushed towards him.

'Josh!'

He threw himself into her arms, clinging to her with so much strength and desperation he nearly choked her. She held him against her, her heart pounding with fear.

'What's wrong? What's the matter? Josh, tell me! Are you hurt?'

He shook his head wildly.

He had not hurt himself. There was no physical damage of any sort, she should have known by the way he was crying. He wasn't hurt—he was terrified.

'What happened? Josh, tell me, what happened?' She heard her own voice, wild with fear, and it seemed the voice of a stranger. She would have to calm herself before she could calm him.

He was too heavy for her to lift up, so she stayed where she was—on her knees on the kitchen floor, holding him tightly until his desperate crying began to ease off a little.

'Come on,' she said quietly. 'Let's sit down in the living room.' Her arm around his shoulders, she gently moved him towards the sofa. He huddled up against her. Today was the first day she had ever held him, ever really touched him. Something had happened, something so terrifying he had to find his comfort from her.

'Tell me what happened, Josh.' She tried to sound calm and in control.

'Oh, Beth ... somebody ... s-s-some lady ...' Bursting into tears once more, he could say no more. His body trembled against her.

'A lady? Where?'

'Here . . . in-in-in a car . . . a big s-s-silver car.' He struggled with the words, and Beth's nerves were so tight it took all her might to stay calm. She hadn't seen a car, she hadn't *heard* a car come up the driveway. The dishwasher, she thought wildly, that stupid dishwasher had blocked all sounds from outside.

'Where is she? Is she still out there?'

'No! She went away. I heard the car when I started running. I . . . I ran away. Sh-sh-she wanted to talk to me . . . she *hugged* me and *kissed* me! Oh, Beth, it was awful! She was horrible! She talked funny and . . . and she smelled funny and I was so scared. She . . . she said . . . she said . . .' He burst into uncontrollable weeping.

She held him tightly against her, wanting to keep him safe, but fear swept over her and suddenly she felt icy, icy cold.

CHAPTER SIX

IT couldn't be true, could it? Please, don't let it be true, she prayed.

'*I don't even know where she is right now.*' Reid's words echoed in her memory.

She held on to Josh with a kind of desperation, as if she was afraid someone might walk in the door and snatch him away from her. Fear changed into rage. But she had to stay calm. She took in a slow, deep breath. She *had* to stay calm.

'What did she say?'

'She . . . she said . . . she was . . . she was my . . . *my mother*!' It was a high-pitched cry of despair. 'She isn't? She isn't! She can't be like . . . like that!'

Like what? She sounded funny, Josh had said. She smelled funny. Funny like what? And then it hit her. Liquor! Oh, God, she'd been *drunk*!

'It wasn't my mother, was it, Beth? She . . . she can't be my mother!'

'Josh, I don't know. I really don't know.'

'I want my dad!' he sobbed. 'I want my dad!'

'I'll call him right now. You stay here and I'll call him.'

Reid could be at any of three places, and it wasn't until she'd dialled the third number that she'd finally tracked him down.

'Mr McShane is in conference,' she was told by a secretary who sounded as efficient and as cold as a computer. 'May I take a message?'

'This is important. Get him out of the conference.'

She had no stomach for pleasantries right now. Undoubtedly the woman thought she was some female out hunting, and she was only doing her job, but today she'd better break the rules, or else.

'I have instructions not to disturb anyone in the conference, and to hold all calls.' The voice was so impersonal, so devoid of emotion, it sounded like a recorded message.

Beth sighed in exasperation. 'I understand the problem, but this is an emergency concerning Mr McShane's son. Get him on the phone, please.'

'Just a moment,' said the computer.

A few clicks, then Reid's voice asking what the problem was.

'He's all right,' she assured him quickly. 'But something's happened and you should come right away. He needs you.'

'What do you mean, something's happened? What?' Concern and impatience mingled in his tone. 'What the hell is going on?'

'I think it's better not to discuss it on the phone.'

'Tell me, dammit!'

She took a deep breath. 'I think his mother was here a short while ago. She upset Josh terribly and he needs you.'

'You *think*?' He was shouting, and she cringed involuntarily.

'I didn't see her.'

'What do you mean, you didn't see her! My God, where were you?' He was shouting harder now and Beth held the receiver away from her ear. 'Stay with him—I'm coming right home! Don't let him out of your sight!' The receiver crashed down and the line went dead.

Beth was shaking all over and it took her a few moments to collect herself.

Josh sat curled up in the corner of the sofa, looking like a frightened animal. She looked down at him, her heart contracting.

'Your dad is coming home as fast as he can. Would you like a drink? Some lemonade?'

He shook his head numbly. He looked tired. He shivered. 'I'm cold,' he whispered.

'Here, why don't you lie down?' She arranged a cushion for him and he lay down without protest. A folded Afghan lay nearby. She covered him up and then sat down on the floor next to him.

'You go to sleep, if you want to. I'll stay right here with you until your dad comes home.' She put her hand on his head. 'He'll be here in half an hour or so.'

His eyelids dropped and he drifted off immediately. Gazing at the small, sleeping face, Beth felt weak with compassion. Five years old, she thought. Only five years old. She swallowed at the lump in her throat.

Arms clasped around her legs, she sat on the floor, almost in a daze, until suddenly she became aware of a dark shape moving past the window. Reid. Her eyes flicked to the clock. He must have broken all records coming home.

He stood in the doorway, seeing the sleeping Josh, then seeing her. Josh woke up as if he sensed his father's presence. He jerked upright.

'Dad!' He flew into his father's arms, breaking into tears all over again.

Beth moved away, out of the house. For more than an hour she tramped through the woods, hoping she wouldn't get lost, not really caring.

Reid was making sandwiches when she came back. A

quiet Josh sat on a stool, watching, his face still swollen and red from crying.

'Can I help?'

'No, thanks, I'm finished. Here, have a sandwich.'

It was a strange afternoon. She entertained Josh in the house, making flour-dough animals. Reid was in his study, talking on the phone. His voice was faintly audible, but the words were indistinguishable.

It had clouded up outside and the wind had suddenly increased to alarming proportions. Beth saw the trees sway ominously under the power of the wind and she had to admit that the raw strength of Mother Nature did not appeal to her. It did nothing for her mood, either. It was depressing.

'It's raining now,' said Josh, looking out the window. 'We're going to have a real storm, maybe even a tornado!'

'I hope not,' said Beth.

'We had a tornado last year, but it didn't do much.' He sounded as if he were sorry, and Beth smiled. The storm was the tail end of a tropical storm that had started somewhere out in the ocean and had already done extensive damage on some of the Caribben Islands. It had lost most of its ferocious power and was not expected to do much harm to the area.

'Dad says our house is very safe.'

'I'm sure it is.'

'Not many people have houses like ours,' Josh said proudly. 'I like this house the best in the whole wide world!'

'I do too.'

She wondered how it would feel to walk back into her own small apartment, to look out over the city from such height, to see nothing but other buildings, roof-tops, streets full of traffic below.

She thought of her office and all the people in it. She visualised each one of them, seeing their faces, hearing their voices. She felt nothing. Carefully she let her memory go back to the presentation, remembering the faces of the men around the long oval table, remembering the things she had said and what had happened.

She broke out in a cold sweat. The feeling of utter helplessness was still as clear as ever, even the shaking, the crying she could feel all over again. She looked at her hands, seeing them tremble.

Why couldn't she give up? Why was she determined to go back? Why couldn't she admit that this was not for her?

Because quitting was for losers, her father had said. All the clichés he had used came marching through her mind again, like an army of soldiers.

Finish what you start.

Winners don't quit and quitters don't win.

Don't start something you're not prepared to finish.

If you can't do it right, don't do it at all.

How many times had she heard him repeat those lines? They were part of her now, indelibly engraved in her mind, her memory and her consciousness.

What would happen if she quit? Nothing. The world would keep on turning. She'd still have her youth and her health and her talents. She would not be wiped off the face of the earth. She would not go hungry, or at least not for awhile. God would not strike her dead.

But she could not quit.

'Look at this,' Josh was saying. 'It's a bear. You like it?'

They had quite a selection of flour-dough animals in front of them—a cat, a dog, a lion who looked somewhat sickly, a giraffe with a piece of wire in his neck, a rhino and a mouse.

'How about a cow?' Beth suggested. 'Or a kangaroo?'

'A kangaroo!'

'We'd better find a picture of a kangaroo, then. I'm not sure how exactly they're put together.'

'They have a bag on their stomach,' said Josh, searching through his animal book.

Beth wondered what Reid was doing, whom he was calling. She wondered what he was going to do about Josh's mother. She'd felt on edge all afternoon. She wished Reid would tell her what was going on.

'I'm going to make you dad some coffee,' she said to Josh. 'You go ahead and try to make that kangaroo and I'll help you in a little while.'

A cup of coffee in her hand, she knocked on Reid's door and entered.

He leaned back in his chair and sighed. 'Thanks. I needed that.' He looked tired. Angry too. He took a sip from his cup, then put it down. 'I'm going to track her down if it's the last thing I do.' There was so much cold determination in his voice that Beth shivered involuntarily.

'What are you going to do?'

'I don't know. I'll think of it after I've found her.' His mouth was a hard straight line and he glared at the telephone as if it were his enemy. 'I haven't got very far yet, unfortunately. She left her apartment a year after she moved in. The pharmaceutical company she worked for said she was transferred to their facilities in California four years ago. That's as far as I got. I called California, but they say she's not employed there any longer and they refuse to tell me any more. Obviously she's back on the East Coast, but where? Her name isn't listed in Washington or anywhere nearby.'

He must have kept the phone company busy these

last few hours, Beth thought silently. 'You think a private detective might do some good?'

'I'm considering it.' He gulped down his coffee and the phone rang. He snatched the receiver. Beth marched out the door, only to hear him call her back.

'It's for you. Friend Jack, I believe.'

'Tell him I'm not here, please.'

Reid did so, very forcefully. 'Yes, sir, I'll do that.' He looked at her as he replaced the receiver. 'I'm supposed to tell you that he needs to speak to you very urgently. He's waiting to hear from you.'

'I should let him wait till hell freezes over,' she said viciously, surprising herself by the strength of her reaction. The emotion Jack stirred in her was truly phenomenal. 'But I guess I'd better get it over with. I'll use the extension in the kitchen.'

She cast a fleeting glance at his face as she made for the door. His expression was indecipherable. Whatever it was he was thinking, he had no intention of letting her know. Why did she feel so defensive?

Josh was totally absorbed in his kangaroo and was doing quite a job on it, she saw in passing. She dialled Jack's number. It only rang once before he answered. Her jaws were clenched, ready for verbal battle.

'I thought you were there,' he said with satisfaction. 'How're you doin'?'

'Your concern moves me to tears.'

He ignored that. 'I heard from the grapevine that you're shacked up with a dude in a cave someplace. What's the scoop, kid?'

It took a moment to digest that. Drop dead, she thought with venom, her stomach churning. She hated him! God, she couldn't stand him!

'It's none of your business what I'm doing, Jack,' she said through clenched teeth. Her jaws hurt.

'Who's the guy who answered the phone?'

'My cousin, Jack. My cousin.'

'Of course, your cousin,' he said smoothly. 'And he's fifty, bald, and wears dentures.'

'And plaid pants. Looks like you, as a matter of fact.'

'That's not nice, Beth.'

'I don't feel very nice, Jack.' She felt like a time bomb ready to explode.

'We need you, Beth. Ross and Kohler want you for their account, not someone else. They've seen what you did in the last two years.'

'You've lost me. Who're Ross and Kohler?'

'The bubble gum people. Don't you ever listen to me?'

Beth closed her eyes, trying with all her might to stay calm. 'If they want me that badly they can wait another week. I'm not prepared to discuss it any further, and that's final.' She opened her eyes and caught Josh staring at her. 'Leave me alone, Jack. I'll be at your service next week.' She hung up on his protesting voice. Damn him! She wasn't going back a day earlier than she'd planned. Not an hour!

'I wish you didn't have to leave.' Josh's voice was toneless. He didn't look at her. His eyes were directed at the flour-dough kangaroo in front of him. 'Dad says he's found someone else to take care of me while he's gone. I don't like her.'

'Do you know her?'

He nodded. 'You know that nice new house when you pass Grandma Daisy's house? That's where she lives. She has a boy who's five like me. I don't like him either.' He looked at Beth with dark revolt in his eyes. 'We'll go to kindergarten together and when it's over his mother will come and take both of us home and then I'll have to stay with them until Dad comes and picks me up. I don't even wanna go to kindergarten!'

'It'll be strange at first, but you'll like it after a while. There'll be other children to play with. You'll make friends.'

'I don't need any friends! I can play with my dad!'

She noticed his hand, squeezing hard, demolishing the kangaroo.

'What does your dad say?' she asked.

'He s-s-says it's important for me to be with other children. He s-s-says I'll like it. How does *he* know?' He gazed down on the squashed kangaroo in his hand. 'See what happened? I wrecked my kangeroo!' Fiercely he rolled the dough into a ball, lips pressed tight in anger. 'I hated it anyway! It was stupid! It was the stupidest kangaroo I ever saw!' Tears were rolling down his face. He pounded on the ball of dough with his fists. 'Stupid! Stupid! Stupid!'

Beth's heart contracted. She pulled him into her arms—a small tense ball of misery clutching at her.

There was a noise at the door and Reid came into the kitchen. He looked at them searchingly.

'What's going on?'

Josh said nothing, but he stopped crying. He didn't leave Beth's lap.

'He told me about the new arrangement when he starts kindergarten,' Beth stated quietly. 'He doesn't want to go to kindergarten. He doesn't want to go to the new sitter, whoever she is, and he doesn't want me to leave.' She said it all in a flat monotone, merely calling off a list of facts.

'Come on, son.' Reid stepped forward and lifted him up into his arms as if he were a toddler. 'Let's talk.'

Left alone in the kitchen, Beth began to clean up the dough. Carefully she put the animals on an oven tray. They would dry and get hard in a slow oven and then Josh could paint them. On impulse she sat down, took the leftover dough and began to mould a kangaroo, complete with pouch and baby, and added it to the collection on the tray.

There was a dull uneasiness taking hold of her. Dismally she stared out the window into the grey sheets of water that came pouring down with fierce velocity.

She loved Josh, but she had not counted on him being so upset by her leaving. She had not counted on these complications. It would be difficult enough to leave here next week, difficult enough after two months of peace and quiet in the country. Difficult enough to leave Reid.

But she didn't have to leave.

She could send in her resignation and stay. There was no doubt in her mind that Reid would like her to stay. She thought of him kissing her, thouching her. She thought of him making love to her. The idea alone quickened her heartbeat.

She looked down on the animals on the tray. She could be a mother to Josh, play with him and read him bedtime stories. She could stay here with the two of them, cooking meals, gathering eggs, making yogurt and raspberry jam ad infinitum, and live happily ever after.

But it would never work—not for any length of time. After a while she'd start feeling restless. She'd miss the challenge of work, miss the creative processes involved. She'd start to resent Reid and Josh, blame them for the loss of her career, fair or not. Everything would go wrong, she could feel it in her bones. Staying here would be a cop-out in terms of her own problems and her own life.

But what about Josh?

Reid would take care of Josh. He'd done so for five years already. There was no reason to worry about Josh. She picked up the kangaroo and examined it, adjusting one of the small front legs. Josh would be all right. Abstractedly she smoothed the back of the kangaroo, thinking about Josh.

And what about Reid?

She didn't really want to think about Reid. She would leave his house, his small farm, and she would leave him. She had to leave him. The facts were simple and straightforward. Staying here would never work. She had to go.

She felt a hollow misery.

The kangaroo in her hands was now an amorphous blob of dough.

Reid was not successful in locating Josh's mother over the next few days. A total change had come over him and she hardly recognised him. He was a silent, angry man who went his way with bitter determination. His face was hard and all the laughter had vanished. He stayed at home, not allowing Josh out of his sight.

The mail had brought a big package of photocopied material for Beth, sent, of course, by Jack. At first she considered tossing it away unopened, but curiosity had got the best of her, as she was sure Jack had expected, and she had opened the package. It was all background material on the new bubble gum account and she had read through it a couple of times, which was a big mistake.

The stream of images and ideas had started flowing hot and strong. Like an addiction, she thought; I can't

keep away from it, I can't put a stop to it. Her imagination, the creative part of her, was difficult to
control.

She was not surprised when she woke up in the
middle of the night, her mind ablaze with verbal and
visual ideas—it had happened before. She was wide
awake. She got up, found pen, pencils and paper and
worked for two hours, without looking up. Exhausted,
she fell back into bed and slept until ten the next
morning.

Reid was not talking much any more and Beth felt
totally discouraged by his lack of communication. As
the days went by she began to feel a sense of alienation.
He was not taking much notice of her any more, as if
she had already left, was not there in his house any
longer.

She slept badly, and couldn't eat. As she sat across
from him in the silence, seeing the worry in his eyes,
seeing the way he looked at Josh, her appetite
vanished.

I love you, she said silently. Please let me help, please
don't be so quiet. But why couldn't she say those words?
Why couldn't she just come out with it and tell him?

This evening again she had barely touched her food.
She pushed her plate away and looked at him.

'Reid,' she began, 'is there anything I can do?'

He looked at her for a long moment, then shook his
head. 'No, nothing.'

No, nothing. Two small words, like bricks through
a glass window. She felt shattered. Her eyes swam.
She stood up and walked out of the kitchen door. The
sun was low and the colours of the landscape had
mellowed in the softer light of evening.

She sat down on the tree stump and stared out over
the wooded hills. Why was she feeling rejected? There

was nothing she could do. What had she expected she could do, anyway? She was leaving in a few days; how could she possibly be of any use to him?

She heard the kitchen door open, then the heavy crunch of his footsteps behind her. He sat down in the grass next to the tree stump.

'What's the matter?' he asked.

'Nothing,' she said automatically.

'I'm sorry I've been in such a lousy mood lately.'

'You haven't found her yet, have you?'

'No. They're working on it.'

'They?'

He glanced at her quickly. 'A couple of private investigators.'

He hadn't told her he had engaged the services of professionals. He hadn't told her anything after the day Josh's mother showed up, only said he hadn't been able to trace her himself.

She looked down abstractedly at her sandalled feet on the thick mat of grass. What if they couldn't find her? If professionals couldn't find her, then who could? What if she came back? What if she kidnapped Josh? It happened sometimes after a divorce—one parent taking children away from the other.

'What are they doing now?' she asked.

'They're in California. No luck so far.'

She thought of all the expense involved—the high daily fees, the travel and hotel rooms. It would cost a small fortune whether they found Josh's mother or not. It could take weeks or months before anything happened.

She thought of Reid's housing development corporation. He'd probably stuck every last cent into his venture.

She looked at him sideways. He was leaning back on

his hands, looking vacantly at the pale blue sky. She wished she knew what he was thinking, what he was feeling.

'Do you need money?' she asked.

He turned his head towards her, looking surprised. 'Money?'

Beth felt uncomfortable. 'Yes, money. Private investigators are expensive, and you've got to consider your company. If you need money ... I have some. You can have it if you want it.'

Reid stared at her for endless minutes. 'Why would you want to do that?' he asked at last.

'Why not? I inherited some money when my father died, and I've never used it. I don't need it.'

She'd never touched her father's money. She didn't want to need it. She could make it on her own, even though her father hadn't thought she could, at least not in any way that mattered. Reid could have the money—borrow it or keep it, she didn't even care.

'I don't need money, Beth.'

It hurt. He didn't need her help. He didn't need her money. He didn't need her at all. She stared out over the hills, trying to compose herself, trying not to show him her feelings.

He got to his feet and stood in front of her, towering over her. Both his hands reached out to her and pulled her up against him.

'Thank you for offering,' he said in a rough voice, then he took her head in his hands and kissed her hard. Her legs began to quiver and she tried to force her face away from his grip, but his hands were like a vice. Tears came into her eyes and she didn't know if they were caused by anger or pain.

Her arms reached around his back and it steadied her shaking legs. His hands relaxed and began to slide down her back, her hips, but his mouth was still kissing her with a rough, impatient obsession. It stunned her more than anything else.

He stopped abruptly, stepped back, turned and marched back towards the house without looking at her, without saying a word.

Beth sat back down on the tree stump, trembling. Who the hell did he think he was, attacking her like that?

Oh, stop the dramatics! she thought angrily. He's going crazy; you're going crazy yourself . . . it's your own fault. You're doing it to yourself.

The morning was bright and sunny, but with some hint of the end of summer in the air. Walking down the long drive to pick up the mail, Beth thought about going home. Home to her apartment, away from Reid, away from his eyes watching her.

She didn't enjoy this walk any more. She'd made it almost every morning, going down to the road to get the mail. She'd enjoyed the fresh smell of evergreens, seeing the wild flowers growing by the side of the drive—cornflowers, thistles in bloom, yellow and white daisies, golden rod . . . so many more. Now everything had lost its shine and a dull pain had set in.

A car drove by as she opened the mailbox. The car was white. She scrutinised every car that came by. Was it silver? Was it big?

I'm more neurotic now than when I came, she thought, God help me!

There was a stack of mail stuffed into the box. She extracted it carefully and bundled it firmly in the crook of her arm. Then slowly she made her way back to the house. Birds chirped noisily in the trees. A big toad jumped off the path back into the undergrowth.

Reid was stacking the last of the wood. The pile had

been waiting for days. Beth smelled the pungent scent of green, unseasoned wood.

'The mail,' she announced. 'I'll put it on your desk.'

'Never mind, just give it to me.' He wiped his hands off on his jeans and reached for the bundle. He sat down on a log and sorted through it quickly.

Beth sat down too and watched Josh, who was poking around in the woodstack with a stick, aggravating the crickets. 'They hide here in the wood,' he said to Beth, grinning. 'They're thousands of them!'

She saw the black crickets jumping around everywhere. The sun was warm on her back. Her glance wandered back to Reid. He was ripping open an envelope, frowning. His eyes raced over the typewritten lines and Beth saw to her horror that all colour had drained from his face. For a frozen moment of silence he stared at the paper, then came to his feet in one great leap.

'Stay with Josh.' The words were a thick, strangled sound, and for a fleeting instant she saw his face, the terror and the rage all mixed up. A cold shudder went through her. Oh, God, what had happened now? Had they found her?

'Where's Dad going?' Josh demanded.

She had forgotten he was there. 'He . . . er . . . he's going inside to put the mail away. Would you like some juice?'

He nodded, attention back on his stick and the crickets in the wood pile.

'Come inside with me, then.'

'Why? I wanna stay here.'

You can't stay here because I can't see you from the kitchen window, she wanted to say, but didn't. Visions of silver cars and drunk females haunted her, but it wasn't something she could explain to Josh.

'Let's have our snack inside today. We'll have some cookies.'

'We can have cookies outside. We eat outside all the time. I wanna stay here!'

'Josh!' Her voice threatened. 'Come inside with me!'

He gave her a startled look, then threw his stick down in anger and marched towards the house. Beth followed him, feeling guilty. She was being unfair and unreasonable and he knew it. She had no plausible explanation. She'd yelled at him.

Now you know how mothers feel, she said to herself. Guilty. It's one feeling all mothers have in common. Mothers were supposed to feel guilty, for thousands of real, imagined or ridiculous reasons, and if you found no cause for feeling guilty, you probably weren't much of a mother.

And I'm only a temporary babysitter, she thought. I show great promise.

Josh stood in the kitchen watching her pour juice, his face angry, his lips pressed together. She put the plastic Mickey Mouse cup on the table and some cookies on a plate next to it. Josh stood stock still in the same place, staring ahead of him.

'I'm sorry I yelled at you, Josh,' she said quietly. 'But sometimes you just have to do what you're asked.'

He ignored her completely.

She turned away and made coffee for herself and Reid. She had no idea what to do with Josh now, at least not anything civilised. If she'd given in to her instincts she'd give him a good wallop on his little behind and tell him to answer when spoken to. Psychologically speaking that would probably be an unacceptable reaction on her part. That was another thing—mothers were supposed to be psychologists as well. Dear God, she thought, am I glad I've leaving!

She poured a cup of coffee for Reid and knocked on his door with a sense of trepidation.

'Come in.'

He sat with his head in his hands in a gesture of total despair.

'Reid?'

'Yes.' He didn't move, didn't look at her.

She put the cup in front of him. 'Here's some coffee.'

'Thanks.'

Standing by the door, she waited. Nothing came. She swallowed, her heart pumping hard.

'Did they find her?'

'No. But I know how to get in touch with her now.'

Wasn't that what he wanted? 'Reid, is there anything I can do to help? Please?'

'No.'

Bitterness filled her. There had to be *something*! Why was he shutting her out like this?

He looked up, meeting her eyes. 'Beth, I can handle this. I know you're concerned about Josh, but you have problems of your own. There's nothing you can do, so stop worrying about it.'

Oh, sure, she'd stop worrying about it in a flash! No use for worry on her part. They could do without her—they were *going* to do without her. Two more days and she'd be back in Washington. She had problems of her own, Reid had said, and how right he was. He didn't need help from a confused female who didn't even know what to do with her own life.

'Okay,' she said dully, and opened the door. 'I'll ask Josh if he wants to go see Grandma Daisy.'

'Fine, just don't let him out of your sight.'

Just don't let him out of your sight. One more time and she was going to scream.

Reid left the house in the middle of the night. She'd been awake for hours hearing every sound in the house, including his footsteps and the opening of the kitchen door. Half an hour later he still had not returned. Every click of the digital clock sounded like a drumbeat. Every minute seemed an eternity. Had he gone for a swim? For a walk? Maybe he'd gone for a walk in the woods and tripped in the dark. He could be lying on the ground somewhere with his leg broken . . . both legs broken.

You're out of your mind, she said to herself. Rufus would be at the door barking his head off. Maybe Rufus had borken his legs too. Oh, Lord, help, I'm going crazy!

Scrambling out of bed, she found her slippers and her robe. She tied the robe tightly around her middle, then kicked off her slippers and put on her sandals instead. It looked ridiculous, but sandals were safer than slippers out in the dark.

Peeping into Josh's room, she found him fast asleep. She whistled for Rufus as soon as she got out the door and he came bounding towards her out of the dark.

'Where's Reid? Come on, let's find him.'

Rufus took off in the direction of the dock and she followed him, taking the path and avoiding the pasture.

A bundle of clothes lay in an untidy heap on the dock next to a folded-up towel. Rufus stood at the edge, looking out over the water, tail wagging.

'Reid?' Beth's voice sounded eerie in the empty dark of night.

'I'm coming.' The answer came instantly, his voice

sounding very close, carried well over the quiet water in the silence.

Sitting on the dock, she listened to the water splashing, the regular rhythm of his arms moving through the water. He hoisted himself up and jumped on to the dock next to her, splashing water all over her.

'Sorry.' He took the towel and dried his face and his hair.

No swimming trunks, she saw. He slept in the nude and he swam in the nude, too. She should try it some time. It was supposed to feel wonderful.

He wrapped the towel around his middle and sat down, shooing Rufus away and ordering him to stay at the house.

'What brings you here?' he asked.

'You were gone a long time. I heard you leave.'

'I couldn't sleep,' he said lightly. 'A swim helps sometimes. Did I wake you?'

'No. I was awake.'

He did not reply. Beth listened to the night sounds, the crickets, the whispering of the weeping willow, the soft splash of water now and then. She could hear Reid's quiet breathing. She could hear her own heart pounding painfully in her chest.

It was past three in the morning and they were both unable to sleep. The letter he had received was like a threat of doom. She didn't know the contents, but she had seen his reaction. She loved him and she was helpless. He was next to her here in the dark, not speaking, full of worry he did not want to share with her.

It was silent for a long time, then he turned his head and looked at her. 'I'm sorry you couldn't sleep.'

'It's all right.'

His face was shadowed. The moonlight shone darkly on his bare shoulders. Beth wanted to touch him, hold him, feel the strength of him. Her body grew warm and shivery.

'Beth ... I wish I knew how to make it easier for you to leave. You have to go back, and I understand that. I don't want you to feel guilty about leaving, about not helping me. You have your own life, Beth.'

She couldn't speak. The air seemed to vibrate with her silence. So many things she wanted to say, and all of them would be wrong. So many thoughts going through her mind and none of them making her happy. It was all the thinking that got in the way of everything, in the way of her feelings for him, in the way of her love for him.

She closed her eyes. She felt herself trembling as she reached out and slid her arms around his shoulders.

'I'm still here,' she said softly.

CHAPTER SEVEN

REID sat so still, she wondered if he had stopped breathing. Then he expelled a deep breath and she felt his cheek against hers.

'Beth . . .'

'Don't talk, please don't talk . . .'

She could feel his restraint, the tautness of his muscles, then the relaxation. He lifted her face with one hand and kissed her with a gentle force that swept her away on a tide of sweet sensation. He drew back after a while and looked at her. In the shadows of the moonlight she saw his face, seeing no worry now in his expression, no anger, because all that was not part of this summer night—it was only her he was seeing now, and she could give him that, if nothing else. They could be together in the warm night under the stars and it would belong only to him and to her.

He had never looked at her quite like that. She had never wanted him as much as tonight, never felt so sure she loved him. It was a dream—and she moved as in a dream, loosening the belt around her middle, slowly rising to her feet, sliding off her robe. And all the time he was watching her with eyes that made her body quiver and her fingers tremble as she took off the long nightgown and let it fall in a soft heap at her feet.

A dream. It must be a dream standing in front of him, seeing his face, feeling the soft breeze touch her warm face, the bare skin of her body. In the tranquillity surrounding them, she could feel the vibrations between them, the flowing of unnamed emotions.

In a daze she saw him come to his feet, leaving the towel behind, his eyes, dark and intent, not leaving her. She revelled in the sight of him, the tall, masculine beauty of him.

His hands reached out and touched her face with gentle fingers, then trailed slowly down to her breasts ... her stomach ... her hips in leisurely exploration.

'You're beautiful,' he said huskily. 'Beautiful to look at, beautiful to touch.' Both hands on her hips he drew her close. 'You're trembling,' he whispered against her cheek.

Trembling ... yes, and feeling a fire spreading through her, feeling her heart pounding against her ribs. Her arms tightened around his back, where water drops still clung to his skin.

'Come on,' he said, moving both of them down on to the thick mat of grass next to the dock. The grass was soft and cool against her hot skin. He was leaning over her, blocking out the moon and the stars from view, but they were still there in her mind as he kissed her, trailing his tongue softly around her lips, and she closed her eyes, giving herself up to the wonder of the sensations flowing through her. His fingers, lips, tongue—sweet torturers as they moved their way along her body until she could take no more.

She writhed beneath him, relishing the feel of his weight. Her hands delighted in the exploration of his body, his shoulders, his chest, his arms. Fingers curled in his hair, she held his head and kissed him hard and with an urgency she could no longer control. He groaned softly and she knew that he, too, had reached his limits of patience.

Thought was gone then. All was motion and feeling and her senses were spinning. Spinning, spinning to glorious heights.

He was kissing her eyes, her nose, her mouth. He drew back a little and examined her face, his head tilted, smiling.

'A woman is at her most beautiful right after making love, they say. I think it's true.'

Beth was aware again of sky and stars and cool grass. 'Mmm. In Finland they say you're most beautiful about an hour after you've been in the sauna.'

'Maybe the Finns aren't very romantic people. Don't tell me that taking a sauna beats making love.'

'Never.' She'd never felt so happy in her life. She moved her face closer. 'Kiss me?'

When they got up the sun was rising.

Her follow-up visit to Doc a month later was less than a success. He examined her thoroughly again, asking too many questions. He was not pleased. He had an unruly mop of silver-grey hair and blue eyes that always had a laugh in them, except now.

She didn't like him wearing his white coat, looking stern and professional. He was more fun sitting at the dinner table in a sports coat, making jokes. That was the way she knew him best. She'd known him all her life, but having a good constitution she hadn't seen much of him in his professional capacity.

She resented his white coat. She didn't like his office. The nurses were too nice. She felt terribly defensive, and heaven knew why.

Head bent, she listened to his speech. Relax. Don't overwork. Get enough sleep. Cut out the coffee. Eat well. Don't skip meals.

I might as well check into an old people's home, she thought bitterly. That's about all I'm good for any more. Twenty-six and I'm ready for the dump.

'Have you considered changing jobs, trying a new field?' Doc asked, and she glanced up, feeling a rush of angry frustration.

'No. I like my work. I'm good at it.'

'You may be good at your job, but maybe the job is not good for you,' he said calmly. 'I think it's time for you to give that some serious thought.'

She looked at him despairingly, saying nothing.

'Beth,' he said quietly, 'you've come a long way already. You don't have to prove anything to anybody. You're not in competition with your brother and sister. You don't have to make it big like your father.'

She stiffened. 'I don't *want* to be like my father! I *never* wanted to be like him! All I want is to do my job and not crack up like a piece of china! There's got to b-b-be some way!' Her voice shook. 'This whole town is full of working women in all kinds of professions holding their own just fine, right along with the men. So why not me? What's the *matter* with me? What's *wrong* with me?' She felt like pounding her fists against the wall, stomping her foot like an angry child. Her body was shaking with anger and frustration.

'There's nothing wrong with you. We can't all be there at the top. We can't all be the same. You shouldn't try to be something or do something simply because you feel it's expected of you.'

'You sound just like Reid,' she said bitterly.

He smiled. 'I'm not surprised. He's not a prime example of the average American executive struggling his way through the corporate jungle.'

'No.' She thought of Reid milking the goat, chopping wood, fishing, playing with Josh. She thought of the small company he had set up and the earth-sheltered houses he was going to build. It was a challenge to him, something worth doing for its own sake.

'I wouldn't know what to do if I gave up my job,' she said, and shrugged. 'I suppose I could find a man, get married, have babies and bake apple pie.'

'What's wrong with motherhood and apple pie?'

'Nothing. I envy women who choose it and are happy with it, but it would never work for me. I know I'd always want something else, too. Maybe I'm too greedy, but I can't help but think that I'd be unhappy in the long run and make everybody else unhappy too. It wouldn't be fair to anybody. I want to be realistic about it. It's too easy to fall in a trap.' She sighed and looked at him wearily. 'Well, there's my philosophy of life. I've got to get back to the office.'

Too easy to fall in a trap. She thought of Reid and all the things he had said. She thought of him standing on the dock with the moonlight shining down on him, of him touching her and making love to her in the grass. In the two days that followed, before she had left, he had never once mentioned or referred to it. It seemed as if it had never happened, as if indeed it had been a dream and had happened in some other sphere of consciousness.

Driving along Constitution Avenue on the way back to her office, she passed the Lincoln Memorial, the Washington Monument, then the White House and the Capitol. Power City, she thought wryly, full of people scrambling for power and glory and esteem. People with so much drive and ambition that their careers took preference over everything else.

'Washington men are lousy lovers,' her friend Barbara often said. 'They're too damn busy saving democracy.' Beth didn't care for generalisations, but she'd once had an experience that fit the theory perfectly.

She stopped at a red traffic light, remembering Steven. At the time she had known him he was a Congressional aide. He was energetic, dynamic and tireless. She admired him. She was fascinated by everything he told her about behind-the-scenes government, about how things *really* were.

The first time she invited him to dinner was also the last. He arrived at her apartment with a bottle of wine in a brown paper bag and his briefcase. Did she mind if he looked over some papers before dinner? he asked. Of course not, she said, retiring to the kitchen to pour them both a drink.

Coming back into the room she found the coffee table covered with papers. She handed him his glass and he said thank you without looking up. She took her drink back to the kitchen to put the finishing touches on a meal that had taken hours to plan and prepare.

Later, as they sat at the table eating their food, he talked non-stop about some argument in Congress that had his boss flying from the rafters. For some reason Beth was neither impressed nor intrigued. His arrogant, egotistical attitude irritated her. He made no comment about the food, asked no questions about her work or herself. Why had she never noticed before how totally self-absorbed he was? Dinner over, he swallowed his coffee down in haste and gave his watch a worried look. Could he use her phone to call a taxi? He had to catch a plane to St Louis.

She was left behind with a kitchen full of dirty dishes. She looked at herself in her long lounging skirt, the blue silk blouse, matching the colour of her eyes, and had felt a flash of pure hatred.

'Well,' Barbara had said, 'you're not the first one. That's the way it goes. Uncle Sam always comes first.'

Maybe the only way to get to the top was to sacrifice everything else. She thought of Josh's mother and shuddered.

Entering her building, she hurried straight into her office, closed the door, poured a cup of coffee and sat down to work.

It was Friday, a long endless Friday. At half past six the people in the office were still there. Someone suggested drinks, and Beth went along as they all went across the street to their usual haunt, a place frequented by other advertising people.

Beth was exhausted. She should have gone home. Sipping her Martini in silence, she wished she'd asked for orange juice or something equally innocuous. Absently she listened to the conversation of the others, not joining in.

'. . . lobby full of nuns and funeral directors. Guy behind the desk says they're there for conventions. Says there's another one in the place—a group of porno writers . . .' Laughter. Someone made a vulgar comment. A dirty joke followed, after that another one. It hadn't taken long. Beth was in no mood for laughter. She felt drained.

Fishing her bag from under her chair, she stood up. 'Thanks for the drink, Bob.'

'Where're you going?' Jack's voice was almost hostile.

'I'm going home.' She raised her hand and wiggled her fingers. ''Bye, see y'all on Monday.'

Outside she found Jack had followed her into the street.

'What the hell is wrong with you these days?'

She looked at him coldly. 'Something wrong with my work? Any complaints about my performance on the job?'

He pressed his lips together, making his face look flabbier than it was. Then he swore viciously. 'I'm talking about your attitude, dammit!'

'Nobody pays me for my attitude, so clear off!'

They were walking down the street towards the office parking lot. The weather had turned dark and cloudy and the sky was about to burst open. Beth quickened her step and shivered. The wind was cold and blew her skirt around her legs. She shivered again.

Today again she'd been the only one wearing a skirt. Everyone's behind had been tightly packed into jeans with somebody's name on the back—Calvin Klein, Diane von Furstenburg, Jordache. One day she'd get a pair of discount specials and wear them to the office and they'd all drop dead. One goal in her life was never ever to wear designer jeans.

She liked wearing skirts and heels, square that she was. Proper skirts, not like the atrocities Kelly sometimes wore, made out of a curtain or a burlap bag. Kelly went to great pains to show the world she was an artist.

Square, square, square. How had she ever ended up in this business? Maybe she really didn't belong here. Yesterday afternoon she'd marched into Kelly's backroom office, finding half the copy department spaced out on the floor smoking grass and chewing bubble gum—apparently waiting for inspiration for some clever lines, an ingenious slogan, some catchy jingle.

Beth had lost her cool and raved and ranted, giving them a lecture on professionalism in the office, on the conservatism of clients, on the danger to their careers if Jack happened to want to pay a little visit.

That was yesterday. Today it was Jack giving *her* a lecture, and she wasn't going to take it.

He took her arm to stop her. 'Let me tell you something, Beth . . .'

She jerked her arm free and faced him. His thinning hair was blowing across his forehead and his tie was swept over one shoulder. His eyes were hard, but she stared right into them.

'No, Jack,' she began slowly. '*You* listen to *me*! Get-off-my-back!' She swivelled on her heel and began to walk fast, going to the parking lot. She found her keys, got in the car, started the engine and roared out into the street.

The apartment was comfortably warm. September, and the heat was on. This was supposed to be the South, for crying out loud!

She made herself something to eat. The weekend stretched endlessly ahead of her—endless, cold and wet. Bob had invited her to go to the Kennedy Center to see a play, but she had refused. Last week there had been an invitation for a party from an old friend, and she had declined that too. She'd toyed with the idea of going back to the farm for the weekend, but in the end she'd even lacked the simple courage to call.

'Come see us when you can,' Reid had said when she had left a month ago, so what was she afraid of?

Her eyes caught the yellow telephone on her kitchen wall. She could call now and see how things were. Talk to Josh and find out if he liked kindergarten, if he'd made friends with the babysitter's son.

Why was she frightened of talking to Reid? Why did she ask? Twice since she'd been back in Washington she'd awakened drenched in perspiration after a terrible dream—a nightmare about Josh disappearing in a silver car, and Reid sitting alone in an empty house, reading a letter over and over again.

Her heart was thumping wildly as she dialled Reid's

number. The phone rang and rang and no one answered. Ten minutes later she tried again. No answer. It had not occurred to her that no one would be there. For some reason it frightened her. On impulse she dialled Grandma Daisy's number.

'I was thinking about you,' Beth told her after she'd answered the phone. 'How is everything?'

'Oh, how nice of you to call! I miss you, you know. But I'm doing fine. Reid and Josh were just here . . .' There was a slight hesitation. 'Did you hear?' There was a funny tone to Grandma Daisy's voice and it alarmed her.

'Did I hear what?'

'Oh, Beth!' It was a sound of distress. 'Josh's mother . . . she . . . she's sueing Reid for custody!' Grandma Daisy sounded frail and helpless, not at all her usual self.

Beth stared at the wall, feeling hollow. She was not surprised. She'd expected something dreadful to happen, and it had.

'Grandma Daisy, I don't know what to say . . .'

'Oh, Beth, and she's rich—really rich. She's married, you know, and her husband is very wealthy, and you know, they get the best lawyers and all . . .'

Was she crying? This big, tall, indestructible woman couldn't be crying! But she was, and Beth could feel the tears coming into her own eyes. Hot, helpless anger set in.

'Sueing isn't winning!' she said fiercely. 'Nobody would take Josh away from his father! It would be cruel and . . . and . . .'

She didn't know how she ended the conversation. She was in her bedroom, throwing clothes in her suitcase at random.

Minutes later she was on the road, the windshield wipers racing back and forth in front of her eyes, unable to keep up with the pouring rain. It was a nightmare of a trip. She could barely see the road in front of her. Missing one of the signs, she had to make a three-mile detour before she was back on the right track. She had to stop for gas and could only find a self-service station, and got drenched in the process of filling her tank.

'Sorry, ma'am,' said the attendant as she went in to pay. 'Hope you haven't far to go.'

'A couple of miles past Cumberland. It'll probably take me all night.'

He pointed behind him. 'There's a coffee machine, if you want some. He handed her some coins. 'Here, on the house.'

She grinned. 'Thanks.'

The rain did not let up. It was a constant river straight from hell. Creeping along the last twenty miles of dark country roads was an ordeal that seemed to have no end. Visibility was nil and at every turn she was afraid she'd end up in a ditch.

It was after midnight when she finally turned into the long, narrow driveway. Carefully she hobbled up to the house and parked behind Reid's red pick-up truck. She got out into the pouring rain and fished her suitcase out of the back. Her feet sloshed through the mud as she made her way to the front door.

The first thing she heard was Rufus's wild barking and moments later the door swung open and Reid stood framed in the doorway.

'My God,' he said in a low voice. He reached out and practically dragged her into the house. Rufus jumped all over her in his enthusiasm and she almost lost her balance. With a few stern words Reid calmed the dog and he lay down on the rug, watching her, his tail wagging.

The water was running out of her hair, which was plastered to her scalp. She wiped a hand across her face and looked at Reid. He stood leaning against the door, staring at her. Why didn't he say something? What was he waiting for?

'Why didn't you tell me?' she asked, her voice a miserable squeak. 'You should have told me!'

His face showed no reaction. 'Why don't you put on some dry clothes?'

'Damn you! I'm talking to you! Don't *ignore* me!' She took a step towards him, muddying the carpet even more, but she didn't care. 'Why didn't you tell me about the lawsuit? It was that letter, wasn't it? The one that came before I left? It was all in there, wasn't it?'

'Did you drive all the way down here from D.C. to ask me that? In this weather?'

She could have hit him if she'd had the strength. 'Why don't you answer me?' Her voice was high with frustration. 'You could have told me!'

He shrugged. 'Why? You had enough problems of your own.'

'I care about Josh! I care about you!'

His lips parted as if he were about to say something, then his mouth closed. Moving forward, he took her arm. 'Come along.' He pushed her ahead of him into the guest room and positioned her in front of the full-length mirror set in the wardrobe door. 'Look at yourself and calm down.'

Her wet clothes stuck to her skin and she shivered with cold, but it wasn't her clothes that he wanted her to look at. It was her face. Her eyes looked wild, and it shook her. There was a frenzy about her expression she had never seen before. She looked like a madwoman.

She was going off her rocker, going crazy. God, she thought, he must think I'm demented!

He was standing behind her, looking at her in the mirror, his expression unrevealing. No mockery, no amusement in his eyes. Well, that was something.

'I'm worried,' she said tonelessly.

'So am I.' His tone was dry.

The admission shocked her. She had wanted him to reassure her, tell her there was nothing to worry about, that nobody was going to take Josh away from him, come hell or high water, earthquakes, tornadoes.

His mouth twisted in a mockery of a smile. 'Don't look so stricken, I haven't given up yet.'

Beth shivered again and saw him frown.

'Now, get out of these wet things, take a hot shower, and I'll fix you a drink. Or would you like something hot?'

'Something hot, please.' She sounded like a little schoolgirl. She felt like breaking down in tears.

'Coffee? Tea? Hot chocolate?'

Coffee, tea, or me? She suppressed a nervous giggle as the silly joke ran through her head.

'Hot chocolate, please.'

'Coming up.' There was amusement in his eyes now. He'd probably expected her to bolt down a double Scotch instead of asking for hot chocolate.

The shower revived her.

Covered modestly in a long, warm robe (thank God she'd grabbed it off a chair and stuffed it in her suitcase), she curled up in a chair. She could see Reid, his back turned to her, busy at the kitchen counter. He turned and came towards her, carrying two mugs.

'Here, this will warm you up.' He handed her a cup and she held it between her hands. It wasn't boiling hot, for which she was grateful. She could drink it now.

'I've had the heat on in my apartment for the last three days,' she said. 'It's like winter. Last week the air-conditioner was still on. Can you believe it?' She drank from the hot, sweet chocolate. 'Of course in the office we were all freezing. They don't switch over from air-conditioning to heating until later. It's done centrally, of course, and we can't regulate it ourselves, even . . .' She caught the lacklustre expression of his face and swallowed the rest of her words. 'I'm sorry. I'm talking to hear my head rattle.' She was making nervous conversation to cover up her discomfiture. Her body felt tense and stiff. Why couldn't she relax?

He shifted in his chair, lifted one leg and rested the foot on the other knee. He was wearing brown leather work shoes, brown corduroy slacks and a red sweater, the sleeves pushed up to his elbows.

Beth ached for him just looking at him, seeing him in the chair in a casual pose, seeing his strong hands, the arms with the dark shadow of hair . . . She didn't dare look at his face as memories sped through her mind in vivid colour. Oh, God, I shouldn't have come, she thought miserably.

'How's work?' he enquired casually.

'Oh, fine!' She felt ridiculously relieved. 'The copy department came up with some really colourful lines. We're trying out two different approaches and I'm working on the layouts. Roughs only, so far. I've found a great new photographer. She's very young, but she's done some fantastic work, and she understands what I'm after. We're on the same wavelength, and that's one big headache out of the way.'

'What account is this? Bubble gum?'

'Yes.' Why did she feel defensive? She straightened

her back. 'I went on a tour of the plant, in Maryland, and it was interesting, really. The people were wonderful. And it's not bad stuff. They use only natural colourings and it has xylitol in it instead of sugar and . . .'

Why couldn't she stop? Oh, God, she would sit here all night jabbering about air-conditioners and bubble gum and Reid was just sitting there not saying a word.

Why didn't he make her stop? Why didn't he tell her what was going on? Couldn't he see what was happening to her, that she was going to pieces right in front of him? She wanted him to tell her everything.

'What are you going to do about the custody case?' she demanded. She was going to sit here all night, if that was what it took.

'How do you know about it?' he asked. 'Who told you?'

'Grandma Daisy. I called you earlier this evening, but there was no answer. So I called her; I don't really know why, and she was in tears.'

'In tears?' He looked shocked.

'Yes. I could hear it over the phone. I . . . I couldn't believe it either. She seems so . . . so indestructible.' She paused for a moment. 'She thinks of you and Josh as her own, you know.'

'Yes.'

'I wish you'd told me about it when that letter came,' she said tonelessly. 'I thought that at least I was a friend.'

His eyes were dark and unsmiling. 'At least,' he said quietly, 'and you know that. But you have enough problems of your own and there's no sense in complicating your life by getting wrapped up in mine.'

But I love you, she said silently. I want to help you, do something, anything. But she couldn't even think of what.

'What's been happening since you got that letter?' she asked.

'I've been having talks with my lawyer. There's not much to say about that. Not at this point anyway.'

Beth felt frustrated by his lack of detail. 'What did he think? What did he say about the case?'

'That he'll take it,' he said dryly. 'And we've been lining up the facts and figures. He's come to the conclusion that I've been a moron by not getting legal papers after Josh was born, stating that his mother had handed him over to me of her own free will while she was in a sound state of mind—something like that. We have no witnesses, no proof. No legal custody was ever established. That's what this case is going to be all about. And she's going to be sure she's going to get that custody.'

'How can anybody ever grant her that? She left the baby when it was two days old!'

'The facts are that *I* took the baby home. She didn't leave it.' He gave a mirthless smile. 'There are many angles to this thing. Twist and turn the facts to your own advantage and the picture looks totally different while you never actually lied. It's the great art of being a prosecuting attorney.'

'Who's her lawyer?' she asked.

'Gene Morgan, pupil of your friend the vulture, Stuart Engleton.'

'Oh, my God!'

'That's what I said.'

'What are you going to do?' asked Beth.

'There isn't much to do right now. It'll be months before it's in the courts.'

'And all you do is wait.'

'Right.'

'They can't take him away from you!' she burst out.

'It's cruel! You've raised him since he was a baby! His mother never showed up! Why would anybody think he's better off with her?'

'She's his mother,' he said dryly.

'So? What's that supposed to mean? She gave birth to him, that's what she did! That doesn't make you a mother in any real sense!'

'I know all that!'

She burst into tears. 'Don't just sit there! You talk as if . . . as if you're accepting it all, as if you're all cool and calm about it!'

'I am not all cool and calm about it. It's eating out my insides every moment of the day.' His words were calm, but she could see his clenched hands, underlining the truth of his statement. 'I lie awake,' he went on. 'I go into Josh's room I don't know how many times each night and check up on him. I sit by his bed and watch him sleep. Sometimes I think I'm going crazy. But I'm calm, yes. I have to be.'

'Does Josh know what's going on?'

'No. I'm going to keep it from him as long as I can.' Reid raked his fingers through his hair. It seemed a lonely gesture. He seemed lonely and alone, and Beth felt overwhelmed by a need to hold him and say that everything would be all right. But she had no power to promise him that and the words would be meaningless.

He studied her face. 'You're exhausted, aren't you?'

'Yes.'

He got up and came towards her, reaching for her hand to pull her up. He took her in his arms and looked into her eyes with unexpected tenderness.

'Thank you for coming,' he said softly.

His words were like a balm. Being in his arms made her tremble with unbearable tension—a waiting, a wanting aching all through her. She looked into his brown eyes, knowing it was all there for him to see; it was all there in her face, but she didn't care. She put her arms around him, spreading her hands against his back.

Something flickered in his eyes. His face had an unfamiliar tautness, setting off a crackle inside her. He bent his head to hers and kissed her, crushing her hard against him with a sudden overpowering loss of restraint, and she felt herself responding blindly, instantaneously.

Reid drew back, breathing raggedly. 'Come on.'

In her room he slid her robe and nightgown off her shoulders, and laid her down on the bed. Shivering, she felt an odd sense of emptiness, a cold numbness. Something was wrong, and she didn't understand it and it frightened her. She listened to his movements in the dark, seeing only the vague outlines of his body as he impatiently removed his clothes.

'Reid . . .' she began uneasily. She shivered again. How could she be so cold so quickly?

He felt warm against her as he enveloped her in his embrace. 'What?' he murmured, his hands beginning a hungry wandering around her body. And then she was no longer cold, her body suddenly aglow with a fever-ish sensation. Her heart beat skyrocketed alarmingly.

'Never mind,' she whispered, kissing him hard. They made love in a frenzy—silently, impatiently.

It was over in minutes. Reid rolled away from her to the other side of the bed, one arm flung over his face as if warding off a blow. She watched him, feeling flushed and warm with exhaustion, her heart pounding hard and fast.

They lay in silence. Beth stared at the ceiling, fighting a mixture of emotions. There had been no joy, no love in their togetherness. She felt bad and guilty and cheap. She remembered the time they'd made love in the dark outside, how very different it had been, how full of love and warmth and elation she'd been.

The silence throbbed around her. She glanced at Reid. He hadn't moved. His breathing was calm and regular. If he had fallen asleep she would never forgive him. Tears were pressing behind her eyes. She turned and switched on the small clock radio next to the bed and rock music flooded the room.

Reid jerked up right. 'Don't, please.' He leaned over her and turned it off, then he looked down on her, supporting himself on one elbow.

'I'm sorry,' he said quietly. 'That wasn't exactly wonderful.'

'I didn't think men cared about how or what or when,' she said childishly, immediately sorry for saying it.

'Don't be silly. You know better than that.'

She averted her face, feeling tears sliding down her cheeks.

'It's not the end of the world, Beth.'

'It makes me feel bad!'

'I didn't force you into it,' he said quietly.

'I didn't say you did! But it made me feel cheap and dirty and . . . and . . .' her voice broke.

'Ashamed?' he offered.

She nodded, closing her eyes, not wanting to look at him.

'I wish you didn't. There's nothing to be ashamed of. We've been under a lot of pressure these last few months. There's a lot of tension and worry in our lives right now. Your reaction, and mine, was perfectly understandable.'

Beth opened her eyes and looked at him. 'I'm not in

the habit of jumping into bed with a man just for the hell of it. And that's what it felt like.'

'I'm not just any man, and I didn't get the impression you did it just for the hell of it.' He began to kiss her softly, slowly. 'You know very well why we made love, Beth. We made love before for the very same reason, but it can't always be the same.'

He was right, of course. But why did she feel so shaken by her wild, blind reaction to his passion? The night at the pond it had been so different—like a dream in slow motion, leaving her euphoric.

'I'll tell you what,' he whispered in her ear. 'I'll still respect you in the morning.'

She pushed at his chest and he drew back, his eyes smiling.

'Don't you dare laugh at me!'

Reid straightened his face with visible effort. 'Beth, a little raw passion isn't going to kill you, you know. There's no harm in knowing you're capable of it.'

She gasped. 'You're disgusting! Get out of my bed!'

His face collapsed and he roared with laughter. He drew her against him. 'Oh, you're such a little puritan.'

'I am not! And let go of me!' She didn't know if she was angry or insulted or what. She didn't know whether to laugh or cry.

He forced her face up with one hand. One arm held her firmly around the back. 'I want to see you laugh first.'

'Never!'

'But you're beautiful when you laugh.'

The way he held her she couldn't move a muscle. He was looking right into her eyes, taunting her with his own merriment.

'I hope you're having fun,' she said bitterly.

'I am. Why don't you join me? It'll be better that way.'

She gave him a long, silent stare, but his eyes never wavered, stayed warm with challenging laughter.

'Do it for me,' he whispered, 'or I'll feel bad and guilty and I won't be able to forgive myself.'

'Suffering is good for you.'

Beth didn't want to laugh. Taking a deep breath, she tried to control herself. She really didn't want to laugh.

'Try it,' whispered Reid. 'You might like it.'

She shook her head fiercely, biting her lip till it hurt. Raw passion, he'd said. Puritan, he'd said. Her body began to shake and she couldn't control it any longer. Laughter came bubbling up like champagne, spilling over. And then they were laughing together, shaking helplessly as it rocked their bodies, until finally they were exhausted and lay back, breathless.

'Now that was good,' he said at last, grinning. 'Feel better?'

'Mmm—much.'

'Not feeling down on yourself any more?'

She shook her head.

'Not angry with me any more?'

'No.'

'Good.' He drew her into his arms and kissed her softly, tenderly, and she put her arms around him, shifting closer. She felt warm and safe and comfortable, and totally exhausted. He kissed her closed eyes and she let out a long, lazy sigh. He laughed softly.

'I've got to go,' he said in a low voice.

'I want you to stay. I want to go to sleep just like this.'

'I'd like that too, but I can't. You understand, don't you?'

She nodded. 'You're a puritan.'

'Touché.' He unwound her arms from around his neck and left the room, grinning.

It was Josh who woke her the next morning, crashing through the door and throwing himself on the bed.

Beth struggled up, dazed, laughing. 'You scared me to death!'

He flung his arms around her, squeezing almost too hard. 'I'm so glad you're back!'

'So am I. I missed you, so I thought I'd come for a visit.'

'I miss you all the time. I think of you every day.'

His exuberant welcome warmed her. 'I want to know all about kindergarten and the lady who takes care of you. Is she nice?'

He grinned. 'She's okay, I guess.'

'Not a real barracuda, then?'

'What's a barracuda?'

'A big mean fish with long sharp teeth.'

He almost choked with laughter and she had to pat him on the back to calm him down.

'What about your teacher?' she asked. 'Is she mean?'

'No, she's real nice. Like ... like ...' Josh was searching his mind for something, she could tell by the glitter in his eyes. 'Like a bunny rabbit!' His voice was triumphant.

'She has long ears and a tail?'

'Yeah!' He snuggled closer, moving his hands two feet apart. 'Ears this long!'

'Oh, boy, she's in trouble!'

'Not really.' He grinned at her reassuringly. 'I'm only kidding, you know.'

Beth feigned a sigh of relief. 'I'm sure glad about

that.' She looked into his smiling little face. 'I guess I'd better get up.'

He nodded. 'Dad is fixing pancakes for breakfast,' he announced. 'Are you hungry?'

She nodded. 'Yep. You run along now and I'll get dressed.'

Josh scurried off the bed and rushed to the door. 'You hurry up, okay?' he demanded as he disappeared through the door.

Pancakes, sausages and eggs were heaped on to her plate as soon as she sat down. Famished, she tucked it all away with appetite. 'You make a better breakfast than anybody I know, and that includes my mother,' she told Reid.

He grinned. 'Wow, that sounds like treason! Your poor mother. I'll promise not to tell her.'

'I'm not worried,' she said dryly. 'My mother can take it.'

He gave her a thoughtful look. 'You haven't mentioned your mother before. Where does she live?'

'Here and there. She spends the winters in Florida or the Caribbean and in the summer she goes to Europe with a friend or stays at home. She has an apartment in D.C.'

Beth took another pancake and poured a liberal amount of maple syrup over it. She hadn't had a decent breakfast in weeks. Making it for herself was not the same—by the time her nostrils had had their fill of the cooking odours, her stomach needed no more.

The entire day her mind was busy with Reid and Josh and what was going to happen. There was so much she didn't know, and it made her feel nervous and uncertain.

'Do you think it would make a difference if you were married?' she asked. 'Do you think they might consider it a better home situation for Josh?'

They were sitting on the dock, watching Josh paddling around in his little rubber boat. The rain had stopped and the temperature had risen sharply and it was almost warm. Reid was chewing on a blade of grass. He didn't look at her.

'Maybe, maybe not. These days they're beginning to consider fathers proper single parents too.' He shrugged. 'Of course some people, judges included, have their thinking stuck in the Middle Ages.'

'Are you planning to get married some day?' she asked. 'Do you want to?'

'Yes, I'd like to.' He threw the blade of grass in the water and heaved a great sigh.

Beth remembered the time when he had told her he was uncomfortable with love—the word love. She wondered what he thought love was; what it meant. He had never loved Josh's mother. He probably didn't love her, either. It was a painful thought.

'Josh's mother is married to a very wealthy man, I hear,' she commented.

'Yes. Wealthy, and very influential in all the right circles,' he said meaningfully.

'We're talking about justice.'

'So are they.' He gave her a faintly mocking look. 'Don't be too naïve about the processes of justice. The more money and influence you have, the easier it is to get what you want.'

'Are you telling me that they're going to get Josh?'

'No, they're not going to get him. They're going to try and I'm going to have to fight, but they're never going to get him.' His profile was hard as granite, his lips tight. 'I'll do whatever it takes. There are ways. I have resources.'

Maybe there was something she could do. Beth

looked at him and her heart began to pound. 'Ask your lawyer, and if he thinks it might help . . .' She hesitated, hearing her own words as if they came from someone else. 'If he thinks it would help . . . we could get married.'

CHAPTER EIGHT

SHE hadn't said that. Those words weren't hers. Dear God, how could she have come up with a suggestion like that? She went hot and cold at the same time. After saying so many times that she wasn't going to give up her career because she needed it, she had to say something like that. It *would* mean giving up her career. There was no way she could commute to D.C. from Cumberland. She was going insane, no question about it.

Why didn't Reid say something? Hadn't he heard? Maybe she hadn't actually said the words; maybe they'd only been thoughts. Maybe he was in shock.

'Are you serious?' he asked, staring at her as if she were a creature from outer space.

Serious? She hadn't the faintest notion. She wished he weren't looking at her like that. She had the feeling that any minute now she was going to melt into a puddle of murky water out of sheer embarrassment.

She looked away. 'I wouldn't kid about a thing like that. I'm not that crude. Stupid maybe, but not crude.'

'It's an idea,' he said, as if considering it. 'To tell you the truth, I've been wondering what they're going to make out of you staying with us this summer. It's not going to escape their attention; I've no illusions about that. They love sexual scandal. *Father conducting torrid love affair in front of small son.* They'll dredge it up like a body out of water.'

'*Torrid!* You had to say that, didn't you?'

He gave a crooked grin. 'I didn't know I could shock you that easily.'

'I'm not shocked. I'm not delighted either about what it'll do to your image as a good father.' Beth thought for a moment. 'They'll make you out as having a bad influence on poor little Josh, corrupting his little soul with your loose, immoral behaviour.'

He groaned, 'Spare me!'

'If it weren't so sad, it would be funny,' she said dully.

'Definitely very funny.' Reid looked at her, eyebrows raised in question. 'What would they think if we got married?'

She shrugged, feeling deflated. 'They'd probably put that in a bad light too. They might think you married me for effect, to make your situation seem more respectable, more stable.'

'That would be extremely difficult to prove, wouldn't it? Nobody could claim I went out for the purpose and fished you up out of some alley.'

She jumped to her feet. 'I don't like this conversation.' Turning, she got off the dock and on to the path and started walking around the pond towards the woods in the back. She felt shrivelled up inside. Some idiotic part of her had asked a man to marry her. It's an idea, he'd answered. Heavens, as if it was some business deal to be considered! Well, that was the way she had presented it. What had she expected? That he'd fall all over her drooling with love and eternal devotion?

Reid was shouting at Josh to get back to the dock and out of the water. The soil under her feet was soggy with the rain. Dead leaves were falling already and the musty smell of wet forest land hung in the air. There were footsteps behind her, heavy, quick

'Beth?' Reid stood in front of her, eyes searching her face.

'Yes?' She was sinking away in the wet soil. Good. In embarrassing moments people always wanted to sink through the ground. Well, she was, but not fast enough.

'Beth, I'm sorry.'

'It's all right, never mind.'

'Let's forget the whole thing.'

Anger exploded inside her. '*Thanks*,' she said caustically, 'you're so kind to let me off the hook!' Her feet made a sucking sound as they extricated themselves from the muddy soil. She marched off, away from him.

Why was she so angry? I should have been relieved, she thought. *I should have been relieved!*

'Now wait a minute!' Reid grabbed her arm and swung her around to face him. 'What the hell is that supposed to mean? You make me a proposal that I find very generous and touching and completely incredible. It was also probably the dumbest thing you've ever done in terms of your own life. You know that. I know that. You'd be sorry as soon as you got your senses back!' He looked angry and impatient. 'What the hell was I supposed to say?'

'What's the usual answer when someone asks someone else to marry him . . . her?' Her voice shook.

'It's never happened to me before.'

'You could have said yes.' She tore herself away and marched on doggedly, her eyes blurred over with tears. Blindly she stared at her feet as they moved along, breaking branches and twigs. Crack, crack.

'I can't ask it of you, Beth,' he said calmly, walking next to her through the mass of wet leaves.

'You didn't do the asking. I did.'

'What would you do about your job? Your career?'

'I haven't thought about it yet.' She didn't look at him. She might never look at him again. 'I'd figure something out.' Thinking about it was frightening. *Finish what you start*, her father had said. *Quitting is for losers*. She didn't want to think about all the consequences right now. It didn't really seem to matter much right now. It would matter again later, but now all she worried about was Reid and Josh. The threat of the court case hung like a dark shadow in her mind, blotting out everything else.

When they entered the house ten minutes later, he still hadn't answered her.

They had dinner. They played a card game, all three of them around the table. Beth made her moves automatically, trying not to feel, trying not to think. She avoided looking at Reid's face, watching his hands instead. It didn't help much. She wished she were somewhere else—Siberia in winter, Purgatory, any place.

Reid made popcorn and they watched television. Josh lay on his stomach, kicking his feet up and down, chewing, staring hypnotically at the tube. Reid chewed and stared blankly at some point beyond the set. What was he thinking? Worry curled around inside her, strangling. The phone rang and she almost jumped. Reid got up and went into his study, closing the door.

Ten minutes later he came back, strode into the kitchen and began to pour himself a drink. Beth followed him in.

He lifted an eyebrow in question and motioned to the bottle of Scotch. 'Want one?'

'No, thanks.' He seemed outwardly calm, but she sensed the tension inside him.

'My lawyer,' he offered, without her asking.

'On *Saturday night*?'

'The golf course is wet.' He lifted his glass to his mouth and looked at her over the rim. 'I can't figure you out,' he said as if she were some Chinese puzzle he'd worked on day and night without success.

'Don't try.' She opened a cupboard and took out a wine glass. 'Mind if I have some Chablis?'

He took a bottle from the refrigerator and filled her glass. His eyes met hers. Having put the bottle back, he lifted his glass and smiled. 'Cheers.'

'Cheers,' she said automatically. Glass tinkled against glass. Then almost in slow-motion Reid put his drink down, took hers from her fingers and put it down too. His eyes didn't leave her face.

'Beth,' he said softly, 'please forgive me my incredible insensitivity this afternoon.'

She couldn't think of a thing to say.

He took her hands in his. They were warm and comforting; her own were icy cold.

'If the offer still stands,' he said slowly, looking straight at her, 'I would like very much for us to get married.'

For a moment she thought she was going to faint right at his feet. 'The offer still stands,' she whispered, without thinking, without considering.

His smile lit up his face. He drew her into his arms and began to kiss her slowly, thoroughly.

Beth drew back, remembering the phone call, and a chill set in. 'Did you ask your lawyer about it? Did he think it was a good idea?'

'I didn't ask him, I told him.'

'Told him? What?'

'That I was going to get married.'

She had to think about that. 'What did he say?'

'He congratulated me.'

'Why? I mean, why didn't you ask for his opinion first?'

'Because I'm not going to have anybody tell me whether I can get married or not. It's private, between you and me, and it's nobody else's damn business.'

The chill had vanished. She smiled. 'I'm glad. I'm glad you feel that way.'

Reid smiled. 'Why?'

She hesitated. 'It makes it seem a little less ... arranged. More personal.'

'It's very personal.' The warmth in his eyes opened inside her a feeling of light and colour and joy. Tightening her arms around him, she stood on tiptoe to kiss him when over his shoulder, movement caught her eye.

'I want some more popcorn.' Against the wall stood Josh, yawning, holding out his bowl.

After that everything changed. Beth had no idea how it had come about. Something different had entered their relationship, something indefinable, intangible. Reid circled around her in a careful, polite manner. He seemed moody and distracted for the rest of the weekend. She was amazed by his attitude, hurt by it. Soon she would be his wife, and he was keeping her at a distance as if she were some Oriental princess not to be touched until the wedding night. Arranged marriages, those. Well, wasn't that exactly what they would have too? Arranged not by their parents but by themselves.

She went back to Washington on Monday to straighten out her life—as much as that was possible, she thought moodily as she drove north on Interstate 95.

She'd made an early start and arrived at work at ten. Not bad, considering the distance. 'I need another leave of absence,' she told Jack, who rolled his eyes heavenward and said something blasphemous.

'Why, if I may ask?'

'I'm getting married next week.'

He swore under his breath and glared at her. 'What do you want me to say?'

'You could try "congratulations-and-yes-you-may-have-that-leave-of-absence." '

He looked at her furiously, but she stared right back at him, pretending she didn't care what he said or did. Inside she was shivering with nervous tension.

Jack slammed his hand on the desk top. 'Couldn't you have waited till the damn campaign is finished?'

'No. It's an emergency.' Wrong words.

'Ah! Now I know why you've been so miserable lately.' His eyes settled meaningfully on her belly. 'Not too smart, was it?'

Beth didn't dignify that with an answer. She swung out of the room and slammed his door with relish, the sound reverberating through the outer office. People looked up in surprise as she marched back into her own office.

She wasn't going to stay here for another minute. She'd intended staying out the week so she could hand over her work in some organised fashion. She gathered her things together in a frenzied fury and dumped them on Bob's desk. 'Here, it's all yours. The big stuff is still in my office. I'll be gone for a while, don't know when I'll be back.'

Without waiting for an answer she stomped out of the office. Jack could fire her if her wanted to. She almost hoped he would. It would make everything easier.

Coward, she thought. Why don't you resign?

In her apartment she tidied everything up, then took

a load of clothes and sheets to the basement to get them washed. Two women were in the laundry room busily folding up their dry clothes on a long table as a constant stream of yak-yak poured from their mouths. They didn't even slow down when she entered.

Beth opened one of the washing machines, set the controls, poured in detergent and dumped in some clothes. '. . . told her it was her own fault for marrying the jerk 'cause . . .' She opened the lid of another machine, set the dials, poured in the detergent and put in the sheets. She repeated the process once more. '. . . her cousin, no, her cousin's friend, and her mother—I mean the mother of her cousin's friend— they all . . .'

She'd leave the washers to do their thing and in the meantime she'd go back up and clean out the refrigerator. No knowing when she'd be back. For the time being she'd better keep the apartment. No sense in making decisions hastily.

Such as asking a man to marry you out of the blue.

Oh, damn! She hated cleaning the refrigerator, hated cleaning windows and bathrooms. She didn't like ironing or polishing furniture. What I need is a wife, she thought grimly, not a husband.

Reid seemed surprised to see her back again that night. She hadn't even thought of calling him, which seemed strange in retrospect.

'I had a fight with Jack and walked out,' she said stiffly.

'You quit?'

'No.' She didn't look at him. She didn't want to see the expression on his face. She felt defensive and it angered her. She had no apologies to make, nothing to defend or justify. Just because she was getting married it didn't mean she had to quit her job or give up her apartment.

Her eyes swept the room, avoiding him. 'Jack thinks I'm getting married because I'm pregnant. I didn't bother to set him straight, I just walked out. I couldn't stand the sight of him any more. He's so damned offensive all the time. I don't know why that's so necessary. He seems to get his kicks by acting the bastard.' She sighed, shrugging. 'Then again, maybe he isn't acting. Maybe he is a bastard, plain and simple. I keep hoping for his soft side to show, but no luck so far. I'm so tired I don't know what I'm saying any more. I'm going to bed.'

The next few days were like a nightmare. Reid was away from home almost constantly now. Beth took care of the animals, the garden, the house. She canned endless quarts of apple sauce, baked bread and cakes and pies and froze most of them. She worked frantically—anything to dull her mind, watching television while she worked. Comedy re-runs, old movies, game shows—people screaming, dancing, jumping up and down like maniacs as they won trips to Paris, microwave ovens, bedroom sets. The world had gone berserk.

On Thursday night Reid came home late.

'Josh in bed already?' he asked as he sat down to have his dinner of warmed-over spaghetti.

'Yes. He went half an hour ago and he's gone for the night, I'm afraid.'

Reid sighed wearily. 'I'm sorry. I hope he didn't make a fuss.'

'He was fine. I read him a long story.'

He gave her a quick, tired smile. 'Thank you.'

He ate his food in silence, then picked up his plate and put it in the sink.

'Beth,' he said in a calm, controlled voice, 'we don't have to go through with this.'

'With what?' she asked, playing dumb.

'With the wedding, the marriage.'

'Don't you want to any more?'

'You're miserable,' he pointed out.

'So are you.'

He was silent.

Beth looked at him squarely. 'I want to go through with it. I'm not good at making decisions, but once I make one, I stick by it. I'm not going to change my mind. You'll have to make your own decision.'

'I already did, last week.'

'Well then . . .'

'We're going to have an extremely difficult time ahead of us.'

'I know that.' She was wiping the counter fanatically.

'In spite of everything, I hope we can be happy. Maybe it's asking for the impossible.' Looking up, she saw a sadness in his eyes.

'Are you worried about it?' she asked.

'Yes, of course I am.'

He was talking about their marriage apart from all the other circumstances of their life together—the custody case, her career problems. He wanted them to be happy.

Rufus, half asleep by the door, raised his head and gave a soft growl. There was the sound of a car and looking out of the window Beth saw the floodlight washing over a dark-coloured Mercedes Benz coming smoothly to a stop in front of the house. A man stepped out, tall and grey-haired, wearing a brown leather coat. He strode up the house, his gait and appearance one of confidence and power.

Reid opened the door before the man could ring the door bell.

The stranger offered his hand. 'Mr McShane? My name is Conrad Rutherford. If it's convenient I would like to speak to you, please.'

Reid's expression grew hard as soon as the man introduced himself. He stiffened visibly and it shocked Beth to see the sudden coldness in his eyes. She felt like a spy watching them, but they were right there in her line of vision as she stood near the breakfast bar in the open kitchen.

'Please come in,' said Reid in a dreadful, formal voice.

Conrad Rutherford stepped inside, his eyes sweeping around the room. 'Fascinating place,' he commented. He smiled at Beth and Reid introduced her.

He was almost as tall as Reid, but older, his hair thick and silver-grey. His grey eyes smiled into Beth's. She felt an instant liking for the man, although Reid's reaction made her feel extremely uneasy. Who was this man Rutherford? From Reid's reaction she'd gathered that he knew the name, but not the man in person.

There was the sound of small footsteps and then a sleepy-faced Josh in pyjamas came into the room. He looked at the three of them, not comprehending.

'What's the matter, Josh?' Reid's face had gone white.

'I wanted to see if you were home.'

'I'm home, Josh. Come on, I'll take you back to bed.' He turned to Conrad Rutherford. 'Please have a seat, I'll be right back.'

Beth came forward. 'I'll take your coat.'

'Thank you.'

Reid came back a few moments later. 'May I get you a drink?' he asked.

'Bourbon, please.'

'And you, Beth?'

'I'll have some white wine.'

Outwardly Reid appeared calm and controlled, but she sensed an angry hostility in him. Conrad Rutherford took the drink with a polite thank you and sat back in his chair. The polite formality was setting Beth's nerves on edge. Something was going on, and it wasn't good. The air was heavy with tension, or was she just imagining it? Conrad Rutherford didn't seem angry or hostile, although she had the faint impression that he was slightly uncomfortable.

Reid handed her a glass of wine. 'Sit down, Beth.'

She shook her head. 'No, thanks, I'll leave you to do your business. I'll be in my room.'

'I'd like you to stay,' he said quietly, looking right into her eyes.

She sat down, feeling awkward. Conrad Rutherford looked uneasy, and Reid gave the man a cool look.

'Anything you have to say she can hear. Next week she'll be my wife.'

'My congratulations.' He smiled again at Beth.

'Thank you,' they said at the same time.

Conrad Rutherford drank deeply from his Bourbon. Then his grey eyes looked straight at Reid. 'Mr McShane, this is extremely personal, and this is not easy for me.' He cleared his throat. 'I want to talk to you about my wife.'

She knew then. Conrad Rutherford was the man Josh's mother had married.

CHAPTER NINE

A QUICK, questioning glance at Reid and the almost imperceptible nod of his head affirmed her conclusion. Her hand with the glass of wine floundered halfway between the arm rest of the chair and her mouth. She put the glass down and stared at Conrad Rutherford. The handsome face with the square chin and straight, aristocratic nose had a thoughtful look.

'Mr McShane,' he began, 'I was not aware until a few days ago that my wife had brought suit against you for the custody of your son. In fact, I was not aware until a couple of months ago that she had a son. She never told me.' He stared into his glass.

Reid's face was cool and shuttered. He made no reply.

Conrad Rutherford looked up. 'My wife has gone through a painful period and these last few months have been difficult for both of us. She was three months pregnant when she had a miscarriage two months ago. It affected her deeply and she seems unable to accept it. We both wanted the baby very much.' He was talking in a calm manner, not asking for sympathy, merely stating the facts.

Beth shifted nervously in her chair, her heart beating uneasily. Reid's face was unrevealing, untouched by Conrad Rutherford's words.

Conrad Rutherford paused as if he had difficulty speaking. 'She began drinking heavily,' he said at last.

Reid straightened his back. His knuckles were white. 'Your wife, Mr Rutherford, had been drinking when

she came to my house to see my son. The confronta-
tion with his mother whom he had never met, from
whom he had never heard a word, was a traumatic
experience, as you may well imagine.' There was so
much barely controlled anger in Reid's voice that even
Beth felt herself shrink back into her chair.

'I can well imagine,' said Conrad Rutherford. He
looked pale and a painful expression crossed his
features. Beth almost felt sorry for him.

The tension in the room was so heavy she could
almost hear it crackle and spark. She was afraid to
breathe. Her eyes shifted between the two men.

Silence.

Why had this man come here? To explain why his
wife wanted her son? Reid didn't care why. There was
no way in the world he was going to make Reid understand or give in or compromise. If he had come to pull
some stunt, he was in the wrong place.

Conrad Rutherford took a sip from his drink. 'After
she lost the baby she began to talk about her son . . .
your son. I think she's been feeling guilty all these
years for giving him up. Now she feels she's been
punished by not being permitted the child she was
carrying. It's not easy to understand all her emotions,
all the feelings that have finally come out. I . . .' he
made a helpless gesture with his hand, 'I'm quite overwhelmed by it all.'

Reid looked stony-faced. 'Mr Rutherford, I'm not
sure why you're telling me all this. As far as I'm concerned, the point is that your wife is trying to take my
son away from me. She had every opportunity to be
his mother, but she declined. For five years she has
never once showed an interest in his welfare. Now she
wants him.' His voice was cold as ice.

Conrad Rutherford looked straight at Reid. 'She is

not going to take him,' he said quietly. 'I love my wife, Mr McShane, but I can't go along with her in this matter. She's too distraught at this moment to know what she wants and what it is she's starting with this suit. Having her son back isn't going to solve her problems. He is no longer hers in any way that counts.' He paused. 'I'll see to it that the lawsuit is dropped. You have my word, Mr McShane.'

It went deadly quiet in the room. Beth sat very still, not believing she had really heard those words. It was all a trick of her imagination . . . a dream. She wanted to look at Reid, but tears clouded her vision and if she moved she would wake up.

'. . . and I only hope that you can find it in your heart to forgive her.' Conrad Rutherford had been talking and she hadn't heard anything except this last sentence.

Forgive. Would Reid ever be able to forgive Josh's mother? She didn't know. His anger was deep-seated, his hostility fierce. And somehow, in a small corner of her mind, she hoped he would. She hoped he would soften his feelings, ease his judgments. But for someone like Reid, with his inborn sense of loyalty and responsibility, it might be too difficult to do.

Somehow they were at the door, saying goodbye. More was said, about lawyers and custody agreements, and then Conrad Rutherford was gone. The car drove off smoothly and they were alone.

Beth was crying from pure relief, tears running down her cheeks. She wiped at them impatiently, smiling, laughing. 'It's over,' she said softly. 'I can't believe it's over!'

'Yes, thank God it's over,' Reid acknowledged in an oddly husky voice. He touched her cheek and a look of perplexity came into his eyes. 'You're crying,' he said incredulously.

'I was terrified,' she confessed. 'Not when I was calm and logical about it, because I couldn't see how they could possibly take Josh away from you. But deep down I was still plain terrified. I couldn't help it.'

'I know what you mean.' He put his arms around her and let out a deep sigh. There was no passion in his embrace, only the expression of joy shared with a friend.

She wished she didn't feel hurt. She wished he would kiss her and make love to her. At times her need for him was almost unbearable.

'Let's celebrate,' he said, releasing her. 'Let's have some wine and cheese and whatever else we can dig up. I'm starved!' His eyes were shining, his step light and easy as he strode into the kitchen.

They had a bottle of wine, pears, walnuts, some Camembert and wholewheat crackers. Reid talked and laughed and told jokes, and the joy and relief radiated his happiness as her own. Only when she thought about the wedding did a small spot of darkness balloon out to fill her heart. She didn't want to think about that. No need to go through with this farce of a wedding, this farce of a marriage. She loved him, but it would never work out, she knew that. She should be relieved. But instead she felt deadly tired. Too much wine? No, it wasn't that. A reaction, probably, to all her acrobatic emotions—the ups and downs, the twists and turns. She wanted to go to bed and sleep for a year.

'What's the matter?'

Reid's question took her by surprise and she looked up at him, seeing his searching regard.

'I'm exhausted,' she said truthfully. 'I'm going to sleep as soon as I finish this wine.' She lifted her glass and drained it. 'That was nice,' she said lightly, coming to her feet. He stood up too, came towards her and took her in his arms.

'You've been working too hard. I feel like a heel. I'm sorry I've been in such a rotten mood lately.'

'You're forgiven,' she said lightly, drawing away from him. She smiled, stood on tiptoe and kissed him briefly. 'Goodnight.'

'Wait.' He pulled her to him again, took her face between his hands and kissed her softly. 'Goodnight, Beth.'

He came to her in the middle of the night and woke her up. He sat on the side of the bed wearing a short terrycloth bathrobe, and she looked at him, groggy with sleep.

'What's the matter?' she asked.

'I can't sleep.'

'You're too excited, that's why—all wound up. Have a glass of hot milk.' She pulled the covers over her face, heart thudding a nervous beat.

'Beth,' he said quietly, 'I keep thinking about you and me, about getting married.'

'We're not getting married.' Her voice was muffled.

'I think it'd be better if we didn't.'

It felt as if he'd stuck a knife in her—a flash of hot, searing pain. 'There's no need for it any more,' she said bravely.

Reid removed the blankets from her face. 'Look at me, Beth.'

She did, and it took all her strength not to burst out in tears.

'I'd feel better,' he said, 'if you'd go back to work, make the best damn bubble gum ads and commercials the world has ever seen, and come see us here whenever you can.'

She nodded, afraid to talk. Demoted from wife to commuter mistress! She felt like screaming. She pulled the covers back over her face.

'Why are you hiding?' he asked.

'I'm trying to sleep,' she said evasively.

'Wake up and we'll celebrate,' he said, and she heard soft laughter in his voice.

'Celebrate what?' She sat up, looking at him, so close to her, wishing she didn't have this strangling feeling of wanting him.

'The fact that we've got our lives straightened out again, and that I don't have to feel so damned guilty any more.'

'*Guilty?* For what?'

'About that wedding, about getting married. I felt guilty because I was using you, and it's not a good feeling.'

'But *I* suggested it!'

'And *I* accepted.'

Beth sighed. 'Well, it's over and done with. You don't have to feel guilty any more. So why don't you go back to bed and you can sleep as peacefully as a bunny.'

Reid didn't reply. He didn't move. He only looked at her, and an intangible current moved between them. It was too dark to see much of his face, but she didn't need to. It was all there in the air around them. She closed her eyes. She didn't want to make love like this—feeling the way she did. She didn't want him to touch her while she felt raw inside.

The silence stretched and finally she opened her eyes, seeing him looking at her, and the pain in his eyes shocked her. He took her hand.

'It's all right, Beth,' he said softly, as if he had known her thoughts. 'I'm going now.' He leaned over and kissed her lightly. 'Sleep well.'

She should have gone home that morning. Instead she found herself cleaning out the chicken pen, the dirtiest of all the jobs on the place. It probably wasn't even necessary. She had no idea. She'd had breakfast by herself; Reid was outside with Josh, working on the truck engine. They'd been there for a while.

A car drove up, stopped near the truck. It was a blue Maserati. Jack!

He got out and said something to Reid, who straightened up and pointed to the henhouse. Jack took the path and came towards Beth, looking around, stopping in front of the house and looking at it for a moment.

'So,' he said when he reached her, 'this is where you've been hiding out.'

She made no comment.

'My God, this place stinks!'

Again she said nothing, worked on, ignoring him.

'Should you be doing this in your condition?'

'I'm touched by your concern, and I'm in fine condition, Jack. Just fine.'

His eyes wandered back to Reid, who had his head stuck under the hood again. 'The guy has a kid,' he stated.

'So he has.'

'Why are you marrying some redneck out here in this godforsaken hole in the ground? Oh, I know why. He got you pregnant. God, I'll never understand you. You must be raving mad!'

Beth was too incensed to say a word. She clutched the bucket of chicken manure, afraid she might dump it all over his shiny shoes. Why was she afraid? Why not just do it? She checked the impulse.

'I can marry anybody I please, Jack,' she said icily. 'I don't need your consent. Come to the point. Why are you here?'

'I was coming to talk some sense into you. You'll thank me for it later, if not now. I want you back at your desk on Monday, pregnant and all, I don't give a damn. You don't need to marry that clodhopper. You can get an abortion, or give the kid up for adoption. There's no sense in letting one little mistake ruin your life and your career. You've got talent and potential. Why for God's sake do you want to let yourself go to seed out here in the sticks? My God, cleaning out a hen house!'

Shaking with fury, Beth could barely get her tongue in action. 'Yeah, I've got talent. That's what you came here for, right? Well, let me tell you something, Jackie-boy! I don't intend to waste any more of my talent on you *or* your lousy bubble gum! I quit! You hear? *Quit!* As in Q-U-I-T, as in *goodbye!*' She took the bucket and turned it over on his shoes. 'Get out!'

Throwing the bucket down, she turned and ran straight into Reid. He grabbed her and steadied her. She caught her breath, hearing Jack's vile curses behind her. She pulled herself free and marched back to the house. With her filthy clothes there was only one place to go. She crashed down the toilet cover and sat down. She was shaking all over.

God, what had she done? She stared at her hands as if there was an answer there. Filthy, smelly—she reeked of chicken manure. She stripped off her clothes and went into the shower, soaped herself up twice, shampooed twice. No job, no husband. Free as a bird. She could go fly wherever she wanted. There was money in the bank—

what her father had left her, which was considerable, and her own savings. All of it responsibly invested, but she could get out what she wanted. Where should she go? On a cruise around the world? A camera safari in East Africa? Japan?

Why was she feeling so wretched? Why was she crying? She didn't want to go anywhere. She wanted to stay right here. She wanted a job, to use her talents, be something, somebody, do something.

She was nothing, nobody. A loser. Didn't have the guts to stick it out in her job, handle a man like Jack, who was nothing more than an insensitive boor who cared only about his own hide, his own purposes.

In her room she dragged on a clean pair of jeans and a light wool sweater she'd bought on a whim the week before and which had cost her a small fortune. The weather was clear but cool and sunshiny bright, whoop-de-do! Beth grimaced at herself in the mirror.

Reid was in the living room, lazily stretched out in a chair, chewing an apple. He grinned as she came in.

'You were wonderful! I loved every minute of it.'

'I'm glad you were entertained,' she said coolly.

'How do you feel? Happy? Relieved? Light as a cotton ball?'

'Like a sack of cement. How do you *think* I feel?' she asked sarcastically. 'I'm out of work. People don't usually feel light as a cotton ball when they're unemployed. I'll tell you what I feel like! I feel *stupid*! I feel like an idiot! I quit, remember? I'm doing a great job of messing up my life.' She looked out the window, catching sight of Josh romping with Rufus out in the pasture.

'Then why did you quit? If it was so damned important to you to keep that job, to prove yourself to the world, to be a great success, then why did you do that?'

Beth was standing up, holding on to the back of a

chair to steady her trembling legs. 'Because I lost my sanity! Because things got to me—like Jack breathing down my neck! He doesn't want to lose his precious account and he'll commit murder to keep his clients happy. You know what it's been like this past month? It wasn't any better than before. They were all on my back again . . .' She took a deep breath. 'I quit supposedly because Jack made me mad. A nice excuse, isn't it? Well, it's what I needed—an excuse. Because I'm too much of a coward to just give up and say, 'Okay, folks, I'm sorry, but this isn't for me. I'll find something else.' You see, James Anderson's children don't give up. James Anderson's children are tough and resilient and they never give up. They make something of themselves. They are not losers. And that's really what I am, isn't it? I am a loser. And a coward to boot.' She stopped, breathing hard to catch her breath. 'It's a good thing my father isn't around to see me now.' She wiped her cheeks and they were wet. All the bitterness and guilt of years was pouring out in tears and words.

She looked at Reid, seeing only a misty image of his bulk sitting in his chair. 'Did I ever tell you about my brother and sister? My brother is a big-time stockbroker in New York. My sister is a financial analyst for a big corporation in Chicago.' It was difficult to talk about them. She had never measured up—not as a child, not now.

Reid looked at her steadily. 'I think it's your father who's messing up your life, not you,' he said calmly. 'If he's still capable of putting on the pressure now that he's dead, I hate to think what he was like when he was alive. Was he ever happy with your accomplishments? Or was it never good enough?'

'A's on my report card were good enough,' she said

dully. 'And then only if they were in the right subjects.'

'And you probably didn't get straight A's in school.'

'Not by a long shot. Maths, science, physics—I squeezed by with C's.' She shot him an angry glance. 'And I don't want to talk about my father. If I think I need a shrink I'll go get one.'

Reid stood up slowly, stretching himself out to his full length in front of her. Anger radiated from him.

'I'm fed up with your negative self-image,' he said, his tone very controlled. He reached behind him and fished a magazine off the coffee table. 'Page thirty-four, wasn't it?' He found the page and thrust it in front of her eyes. Last year's ad, still running, most of it her work. 'You did this, didn't you? That's because you're such a loser, because you can't do much of anything right.' He paused and his eyes bored into hers. 'You have this jerk of a Jack hanging on the phone every other day begging you to come back to work. He even *drives* all the way down here to get you back, complete with all the solutions to all your problems. That's because you're such a loser!'

'Shut up!' She turned on trembling legs, but he grasped her wrist and forced her down into a chair.

'I haven't finished yet!' It took a visible effort to control himself. 'You feel like a coward, you say. That's why you suggested we get married, right? Because you're such a coward!' His eyes flashed. 'Don't you recognise your own worth? Don't you recognise that when things get really tough you shape up into a soldier? What went on in your head when you suggested we get married? It was Josh, wasn't it? You did it for Josh and me! And I don't think that at that moment you even thought about yourself, about what it meant in terms of your own life!'

'I'm such a good Samaritan.' Her voice squeaked.

'Stop the sarcasm! Only a few months ago you came here, knowing nothing about country life, and what were you doing that last week before you left and this past week again? You *ran* the place! You did *everything*! I was nowhere, running around in a panic and you held all of us together. You took care of those animals out there. You made sure the vegetables didn't rot away. You took over without one complaint, without even having been asked.' He looked straight at her, holding her glance. 'Tell me, Beth,' he said slowly, 'does that sound like a loser? A coward?'

Her heart was racing. 'I just did it,' she said evasively.

'Exactly. You just did it.'

Silence. He stood there, waiting.

'What do you want me to say?'

He shrugged. 'I'm trying to tell you that *I* don't think you're a loser or a coward. That *I* don't think your not being able to survive out there in the jungle is any reflection on your value as a human being. And if *I* could do it, I'd just love to pound some self-esteem and self-confidence into that head of yours. You have choices and options with your skills and talents, if only you'd believe it yourself.' He moved away from her. 'Think about it.' He marched out the door, and Beth stared after him, then sank into a chair.

The day passed in a blur.

'I'll leave in the morning,' she told him at dinner.

Reid's face was impassive, but Josh's registered disappointment. 'Can't you stay until Monday?'

She was immensely grateful they had not told Josh about the wedding yet. He was not expecting her to stay for good.

'I'm sorry,' she said, 'but I can't, Josh.'

'Can I come with you and see your apartment?'

'Not this time. But another time would be nice. I could take you to the zoo, or to the Space Museum, and I could show you the White House where the President lives.'

'Oh, wow!' His whole face was shining with excitement. 'Can I, Dad?'

Reid grinned. 'Of course.'

'Have you never taken him to Washington?' she asked.

He shook his head. 'When you live here it seems to be very far away, another world, so to speak.'

I know what you mean, she thought, taking the last bite of her lasagna.

After Josh was in bed she curled up with a book in front of the fire. Reid was in his study. Was he avoiding her? She wasn't sure. But one thing was certain: there was an uneasiness between them, a coolness. She tried to ignore it. There was enough to worry about right now.

Next morning everything seemed different. Something had happened in the night, she knew not what. She'd slept like a rock, like she hadn't slept in years.

This is me, she said to herself in the mirror, a free me, a new me. No more Jack, no more angry clients, no more job. Why had she panicked? There was enough money in the bank to last her for a while. She wouldn't starve. She had all the time in the world to find out what she really wanted to do with herself.

'One thing I pledge,' she said out loud to herself in the mirror, looking appropriately solemn, 'I will never ever again work on bubble gum promotions . . . jewellery . . . perfume.'

On impulse she got back into bed. She wanted to think quietly for a while.

She was going to do something different. She could even go back to school. She wanted to do something fascinating and important, something she would enjoy doing, as Reid was enjoying his risky venture with earth-sheltered houses. It might fail altogether. Nobody might want to buy any of his houses, but he was doing it because he thought it was worth the risk, and because it was something he wanted to try.

The construction would start soon. And then the real adventure would begin. Beth wished she could be part of it in some way, share the excitement, the adventure.

She lay in bed, visualising the building of the houses, the progress from day to day. Her mind produced vivid pictures of beautifully designed homes blending in with their natural surroundings, their south-facing windows set in wood and fieldstone walls. Bright living rooms and kitchens, no darkness.

People would love those houses—they'd have to. There was no reason at all why not.

Excitement coursed through her as an idea began to take shape. Her heart began to pound and she suddenly felt herself grow warm. Why had she never thought of that? She could do the advertising and publicity . . . she could do it alone . . . she could be in charge herself, hire a few people to help her . . . and there'd be nobody but Reid to answer to . . .

She was sitting straight up in bed with excitement, feeling almost lightheaded with it. Letting out a long sigh, she relaxed and lay back down. Why hadn't the idea occurred to her before? All along it had been right there in front of her eyes and she'd been too blind to see, too wrapped up in her problems to see the solution.

But I don't have the job, she thought suddenly. I'll

have to get it, and it isn't for me to decide . . . What if Reid didn't want her? What if he wanted somebody else? No, she would have known about that. He hadn't decided anything about advertising and promotion yet.

She wanted the job, but she felt spasms of fear and uncertainty. How was she going to go about it? If she asked him straight out there were several answers he could give her. One: he could tell her no, and she didn't know if she could handle that. Two: he could say yes, but do so only out of charity, and that would be just as intolerable. Three: he could say yes because he really did want her for the job, but why then hadn't he asked her himself? And how would she ever know if he really meant it?

There had to be a different way. When Josh came into her room a little later she knew what to do.

Breakfast over and Josh sent out to play, Beth poured herself another mug of coffee and sat back down at the kitchen table. Reid was reading the *Sunday Post* and she watched him silently for a few moments, too nervous to speak.

He looked up. 'You want some of this?' He shoved several of the newspaper sections towards her.

'I think I've found a new job,' she said with a sudden spurt of courage.

Eyebrows rose in surprise. 'That was fast work!'

'I'm not sure yet,' she added. Her heart was hammering so loudly, she was sure he had to hear it. 'It's not really decided yet.'

'Tell me about it.'

She swallowed hard. 'It's part advertising, part public relations with a very small company, not an agency. I'll be in charge of everything myself and I'll only have to answer to one person. It's just right for me.'

The silence thundered in her ears and she'd never been so frightened in her life. Reid looked at her steadily for a few moments, his face expressionless.

'You've got it,' he said then, cool as spring water.

She stared at him in motionless relief. 'You mean it?'

'Of course. The job's been waiting for you for a long time.'

'Why didn't you tell me?'

'Because you had to decide what you wanted to do with yourself and your career. As long as you were reaching for the stars, you wouldn't have wanted it anyway. It isn't exactly a big-time job.'

'It could be. If we can sell those houses, you can start a bigger development, a whole town! You'll be famous!'

He groaned. 'Spare me!'

She laughed. 'Well, *I'm* going to try. I'll write the best ads you've ever seen. You want TV commercials? Actually there might be a . . .'

He threw his head back and laughed out loud. 'This is Sunday. I don't work on Sundays.'

'All right. I . . .' she hesitated. 'Reid, are you sure you want me to have this job? You're not doing it for some other reason?'

He frowned. 'Such as what?'

'Well, maybe you feel you should help me. Maybe you're an altruist, a philantropist, a do-gooder.'

He grinned. 'You can forget that. My work is too dear to me to ruin it by doing something unnecessarily dumb. I know exactly who I want.' He smiled into her eyes. 'You,' he said with emphasis.

He wasn't only talking about the job, she was well aware of that, and a stirring began inside her, changing into waves of love and longing as she looked at his face, seeing the sudden darkness in his eyes, remembering making love . . . She lowered her glance and stared at her hands clasped around the coffee cup.

'I'll have to find an apartment in Richmond,' she said, her voice sounding forced and unnatural.

'You can stay here, you know that.' Reid took one of her hands and held it. Beth raised her face and looked at him silently.

'I love you,' he said.

She began to cry. She had not expected him to ever say those words, and to hear them now broke loose a tidal wave of relief. He jumped to his feet and came around the table and pulled her up into his arms.

'Don't cry,' he said huskily. 'I want you to be happy.'

'I am.' It was hard to stop the crying, but at last she did. She leaned against him, exhausted, but filled with sweet euphoria. 'I didn't think you'd ever tell me that. You told me it made you uncomfortable.'

'It did. But not any more. It means something to me now.' His voice was strong and sure. 'But when I first realised it, it was agony. I knew you had to be free and I had to let you go, but I was afraid I'd lose you.'

'Oh, Reid . . .' She smiled and lifted her face to look at him. 'I love you, but you knew that already, didn't you?'

He nodded. 'Last week, when you came back here in that horrible rainstorm, when you were so angry, then I knew.' His arms tightened around her and he began to kiss her—warm sensuous, loving kisses. 'Why don't we get married?' he whispered against her mouth.

Her heart gave a leap of joy. Everything was right, beautifully right—almost too much to comprehend.

Drawing back a little, she looked into his eyes, smiling. 'Are you serious?'

Something flickered in his eye, a glimmer of memory, a faint smile. 'I wouldn't kid about a thing like that.'

'It's an idea,' she said.